S0-AWP-227

elevate science

SAVVAS
LEARNING COMPANY

AUTHORS

You're an author!

As you write in this science book, your answers and personal discoveries will be recorded for you to keep, making this book unique to you. That is why you are one of the primary authors of this book.

✏ **In the space below, print your name, school, town, and state. Then write a short autobiography that includes your interests and accomplishments.**

YOUR NAME ....

SCHOOL ....

TOWN, STATE ....

AUTOBIOGRAPHY ....

Your Photo

SAVVAS
LEARNING COMPANY

ISBN-13: 978-1-418-31044-8
ISBN-10:   1-418-31044-1
4   21

Program Authors

ZIPPORAH MILLER, Ed.D.
Coordinator for K-12 Science Programs, Anne Arundel County Public Schools
Dr. Zipporah Miller currently serves as the Senior Manager for Organizational Learning with the Anne Arundel County Public School System. Prior to that she served as the K-12 Coordinator for science in Anne Arundel County. She conducts national training to science stakeholders on the Next Generation Science Standards. Dr. Miller also served as the Associate Executive Director for Professional Development Programs and conferences at the National Science Teachers Association (NSTA) and served as a reviewer during the development of Next Generation Science Standards. Dr. Miller holds a doctoral degree from the University of Maryland College Park, a master's degree in school administration and supervision from Bowie State University and a bachelor's degree from Chadron State College.

MICHAEL J. PADILLA, Ph.D.
Professor Emeritus, Eugene P. Moore School of Education, Clemson University, Clemson, South Carolina
Michael J. Padilla taught science in middle and secondary schools, has more than 30 years of experience educating middle-school science teachers, and served as one of the writers of the 1996 U.S. National Science Education Standards. In recent years Mike has focused on teaching science to English Language Learners. His extensive experience as Principal Investigator on numerous National Science Foundation and U.S. Department of Education grants resulted in more than $35 million in funding to improve science education. He served as president of the National Science Teachers Association, the world's largest science teaching organization, in 2005–6.

MICHAEL E. WYSESSION, Ph.D
Professor of Earth and Planetary Sciences, Washington University, St. Louis, Missouri
Author of more than 100 science and science education publications, Dr. Wysession was awarded the prestigious National Science Foundation Presidential Faculty Fellowship and Packard Foundation Fellowship for his research in geophysics, primarily focused on using seismic tomography to determine the forces driving plate tectonics. Dr. Wysession is also a leader in geoscience literacy and education; he is the chair of the Earth Science Literacy Initiative, the author of several popular video lectures on geology in the *Great Courses* series, and a lead writer of the *Next Generation Science Standards**.

REVIEWERS

Program Consultants

Carol Baker
Science Curriculum

Dr. Carol K. Baker is superintendent for Lyons Elementary K-8 School District in Lyons, Illinois. Prior to this, she was Director of Curriculum for Science and Music in Oak Lawn, Illinois. Before this she taught Physics and Earth Science for 18 years. In the recent past, Dr. Baker also wrote assessment questions for ACT (EXPLORE and PLAN), was elected president of the Illinois Science Teachers Association from 2011–2013, and served as a member of the Museum of Science and Industry (Chicago) advisory board. She is a writer of the Next Generation Science Standards. Dr. Baker received her B.S. in Physics and a science teaching certification. She completed her master's of Educational Administration (K-12) and earned her doctorate in Educational Leadership.

Jim Cummins
ELL

Dr. Cummins's research focuses on literacy development in multilingual schools and the role technology plays in learning across the curriculum. *Elevate Science* incorporates research-based principles for integrating language with the teaching of academic content based on Dr. Cummins's work.

Elfrieda Hiebert
Literacy

Dr. Hiebert, a former primary-school teacher, is President and CEO of TextProject, a non-profit aimed at providing open-access resources for instruction of beginning and struggling readers, She is also a research associate at the University of California Santa Cruz. Her research addresses how fluency, vocabulary, and knowledge can be fostered through appropriate texts, and her contributions have been recognized through awards such as the Oscar Causey Award for Outstanding Contributions to Reading Research (Literacy Research Association, 2015), Research to Practice award (American Educational Research Association, 2013), and the William S. Gray Citation of Merit Award for Outstanding Contributions to Reading Research (International Reading Association, 2008).

Content Reviewers

Alex Blom, Ph.D.
Associate Professor
Department Of Physical Sciences
Alverno College
Milwaukee, Wisconsin

Joy Branlund, Ph.D.
Department of Physical Science
Southwestern Illinois College
Granite City, Illinois

Judy Calhoun
Associate Professor
Physical Sciences
Alverno College
Milwaukee, Wisconsin

Stefan Debbert
Associate Professor of Chemistry
Lawrence University
Appleton, Wisconsin

Diane Doser
Professor
Department of Geological Sciences
University of Texas at El Paso
El Paso, Texas

Rick Duhrkopf, Ph.D.
Department of Biology
Baylor University
Waco, Texas

Jennifer Liang
University of Minnesota Duluth
Duluth, Minnesota

Heather Mernitz, Ph.D.
Associate Professor of Physical Sciences
Alverno College
Milwaukee, Wisconsin

Joseph McCullough, Ph.D.
Cabrillo College
Aptos, California

Katie M. Nemeth, Ph.D.
Assistant Professor
College of Science and Engineering
University of Minnesota Duluth
Duluth, Minnesota

Maik Pertermann
Department of Geology
Western Wyoming Community College
Rock Springs, Wyoming

Scott Rochette
Department of the Earth Sciences
The College at Brockport
State University of New York
Brockport, New York

David Schuster
Washington University in St Louis
St. Louis, Missouri

Shannon Stevenson
Department of Biology
University of Minnesota Duluth
Duluth, Minnesota

Paul Stoddard, Ph.D.
Department of Geology and Environmental Geosciences
Northern Illinois University
DeKalb, Illinois

Nancy Taylor
American Public University
Charles Town, West Virginia

Teacher Reviewers

Rita Armstrong
Los Cerritos Middle School
Thousand Oaks, California

Tyler C. Britt, Ed.S.
Curriculum & Instructional
Practice Coordinator
Raytown Quality Schools
Raytown, Missouri

Holly Bowser
Barstow High School
Barstow, California

David Budai
Coachella Valley Unified School District
Coachella, California

A. Colleen Campos
Grandview High School
Aurora, Colorado

Jodi DeRoos
Mojave River Academy
Colton, California

Colleen Duncan
Moore Middle School
Redlands, California

Nicole Hawke
Westside Elementary
Thermal, California

Margaret Henry
Lebanon Junior High School
Lebanon, Ohio

Ashley Humphrey
Riverside Preparatory Elementary
Oro Grande, California

Adrianne Kilzer
Riverside Preparatory Elementary
Oro Grande, California

Danielle King
Barstow Unified School District
Barstow, California

Kathryn Kooyman
Riverside Preparatory Elementary
Oro Grande, California

Esther Leonard M.Ed. and L.M.T.
Gifted and Talented Implementation Specialist
San Antonio Independent School District
San Antonio, Texas

Diana M. Maiorca, M.Ed.
Los Cerritos Middle School
Thousand Oaks, California

Kevin J. Maser, Ed.D.
H. Frank Carey Jr/Sr High School
Franklin Square, New York

Corey Mayle
Brogden Middle School
Durham, North Carolina

Keith McCarthy
George Washington Middle School
Wayne, New Jersey

Rudolph Patterson
Cobalt Institute of Math and Science
Victorville, California

Yolanda O. Peña
John F. Kennedy Junior High School
West Valley City, Utah

Stacey Phelps
Mojave River Academy
Oro Grande, California

Susan Pierce
Bryn Mawr Elementary
Redlands Unified School District
Redlands, California

Cristina Ramos
Mentone Elementary School
Redlands Unified School District
Mentone, California

Mary Regis
Franklin Elementary School
Redlands, California

Bryna Selig
Gaithersburg Middle School
Gaithersburg, Maryland

Pat (Patricia) Shane, Ph.D.
STEM & ELA Education Consultant
Chapel Hill, North Carolina

Elena Valencia
Coral Mountain Academy
Coachella, California

Janelle Vecchio
Mission Elementary School
Redlands, California

Brittney Wells
Riverside Preparatory Elementary
Oro Grande, California

Kristina Williams
Sequoia Middle School
Newbury Park, California

Safety Reviewers

Douglas Mandt, M.S.
Science Education Consultant
Edgewood, Washington

Juliana Textley, Ph.D.
Author, NSTA books on school science safety
Adjunct Professor
Lesley University
Cambridge, Massachusetts

California Spotlight
Instructional Segment 3

TOPICS
6–8

California's Changes Over Time

TOPIC
6 Genes and Heredity 8

Investigative Phenomenon How can you use models to describe how changes to genes may affect organisms?

MS-LS3-1, MS-LS4-4, MS-LS4-5, EP&CIIa, EP&CIIc

HANDS-ON LABS

Connect
Investigate
Demonstrate

HANDS-ON LABS

иConnect
иInvestigate
иDemonstrate

HANDS-ON LABS

иConnect
иInvestigate
иDemonstrate

Go to SavvasRealize.com to access your digital course.

Elevate Science combines the best science narrative with a robust online program. Throughout the lessons, digital support is presented at point of use to enhance your learning experience.

Online Resources

Savvas Realize™ is your online science class. This digital-learning environment includes:

- Student eTEXT
- Instructor eTEXT
- Project-Based Learning
- Virtual Labs
- Interactivities
- Videos
- Assessments
- Study Tools
- and more!

Digital Features

 VIDEO

 INTERACTIVITY

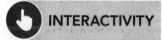 **VIRTUAL LAB**

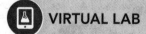 **ASSESSMENT**

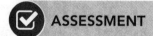 **eTEXT**

 APP

Keep an eye out for these **icons**, which indicate the different ways your textbook is enhanced online.

Digital activities are located throughout the narrative to deepen your understanding of scientific concepts.

 INTERACTIVITY

Interpret models of relationships in various ecosystems.

Elevate your thinking!

California Elevate Science takes science to a whole new level and lets you take ownership of your learning. Explore science in the world around you. Investigate how things work. Think critically and solve problems! *California Elevate Science* helps you think like a scientist, so you're ready for a world of discoveries.

Exploring California

California spotlights explore California phenomena. Topic Quests help connect lesson concepts together and reflect 3-dimensional learning.

- Science concepts organized around phenomena
- Topics weave together 3-D learning
- Engineering focused on solving problems and improving designs

Student Discourse

California Elevate Science promotes active discussion, higher order thinking and analysis and prepares you for high school through:

- High-level write-in prompts
- Evidence-based arguments
- Practice in speaking and writing

California Spotlight
Instructional Segment 2

Before the Topics
Identify the Problem

California Flood Management

Phenomenon In February of 2017, workers at the Orov...

Quest KICKOFF

How can you use solids, liquids, and gases to lift a car?

STEM Phenomenon Auto mechanics often need to go under cars to repair the parts in the under-carriage, such as the shocks and exhaust ...

Model It

Crystalline and Amorphous Solids
Figure 5 A pat of butter is an amorphous solid. The particles that make up the butter are not arranged in a regular pattern. The sapphire gem stones are crystalline solids. Draw what you think the particles look like in a crystalline solid.

☑ READING CHECK Explain
In your own words, explain the main differences between crystalline solids and amorphous solids.

Quest CHECK-IN

In this lesson, you learned what happens to the particles of substances during melting, freezing, evaporation, boiling, condensation, and sublimation. You also thought about how thermal energy plays a role in these changes of state.

Predict Why do you need to take the temperature of the surroundings into consideration when designing a system with materials that can change state?

Academic Vocabulary

In orange juice, bits of pulp are suspended in liquid. Explain what you think *suspended* means.

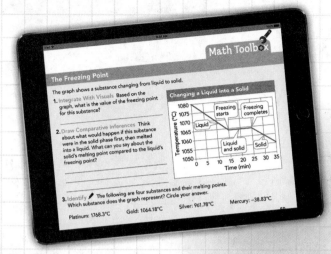

Build Literacy Skills

By connecting science to other disciplines like:

- Mathematics
- Reading and Writing
- STEM/Engineering

Focus on Inquiry

Case studies put you in the shoes of a scientist to solve real-world mysteries using real data. You will be able to:

- Analyze data
- Formulate claims
- Build evidence-based arguments

Case Study

MS-PS1-4

RISING to the OCCASION:
Charles's Law in the Oven!

Have you ever baked bread or rolls? If so, you probably observed that during baking, the bread rises, increasing in volume. What causes this to happen? The answer lies in chemistry.

Chemistry in Baking

Chemistry and baking go together naturally. In fact, chemistry affects every aspect of preparing food.

In the heat of an oven, gas bubbles in bread

Enter the Digital Classroom

Virtual labs, 3-D expeditions, and dynamic videos take science beyond the classroom.

- Open-ended virtual labs
- Google Expeditions and field trips
- NBC Learn videos

NBC LEARN ▶ VIDEO

After watching the Quest Kickoff video about how coastal engineers study and reduce coastal erosion, complete the 3-2-1 activity.

How have living populations changed over time in response to environmental changes?

Explore It

Look at the picture. What do you observe? What questions do you have about the phenomenon? Write your observations and questions in the space below.

MS-LS3-1, MS-LS4-1, MS-LS4-2,
MS-LS4-4, MS-LS4-6, MS-ESS1-4,
EP&CIIa, EP&CIIc

Inquiry

- What can we infer about the history of Earth and life on Earth from the clues we can uncover in rock layers and the fossil record?
- What evidence supports Darwin's theory of biological evolution?
- How do evolution and natural selection explain life's unity and diversity?

Topics

During the Cambrian Period, the land that now makes up California was not yet part of North America. The area that now makes up the White-Inyo mountain range along the border of California and Nevada near Bishop was once covered by a shallow sea.

Before the Topics
Identify the Problem

California's Changes Over Time

Phenomenon Californians are always on the move. And so is the ground beneath their feet. Over millions of years, the land that makes up California has changed both its position on Earth and its location relative to the rest of what is now North America.

The oldest rock in the state dates from about 1.7 billion years ago. Life started to appear in what is now California about 570 million years ago, during the Cambrian Period.

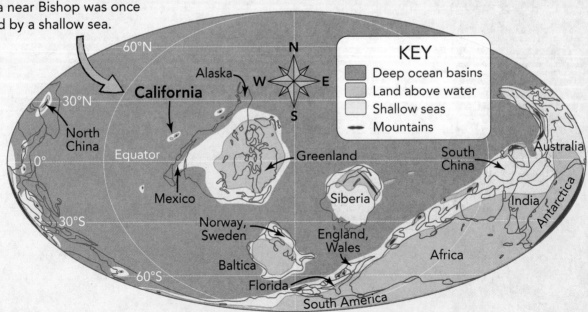

KEY
- Deep ocean basins
- Land above water
- Shallow seas
- Mountains

Changes in Rocks

Earth's surface is always changing. Land is constantly forged and destroyed by forces in the rock cycle, shifting tectonic plates, and other system processes. The fossil record indicates that California's present location and composition are the result of geological changes to the Earth's surface. While California's oldest rocks do not contain fossils, some younger rocks contain fossils from marine organisms. The fossils found in these rocks provide evidence to scientists that parts of California could have once been parts of former oceanic plates that collided into a continental plate. Rock record evidence reveals that volcanic activity and continental sediments formed much of California's land.

Today, many different types of rock make up the land that is California. Each rock type was made during a different period in Earth's history. Recent research finds that the rock cycle, particularly changes in the Earth's crust, played a key role in the start of life on the planet. Without these changes, complex life forms could not have developed on Earth.

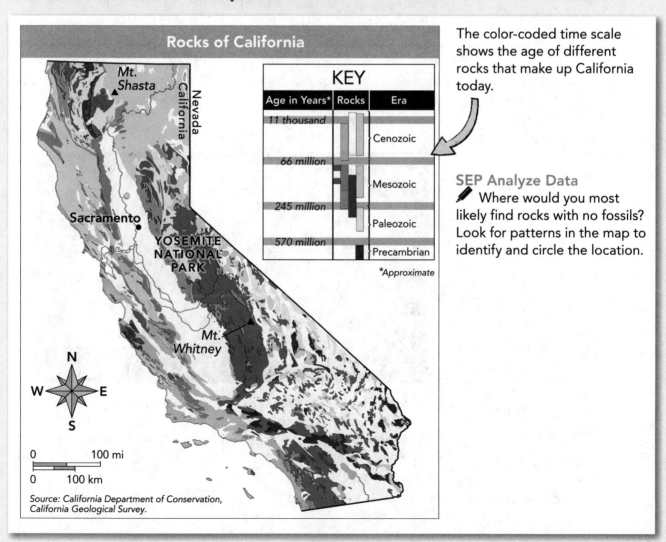

Rocks of California

KEY

Age in Years*	Rocks	Era
11 thousand		
		Cenozoic
66 million		
		Mesozoic
245 million		
		Paleozoic
570 million		
		Precambrian

*Approximate

Source: California Department of Conservation, California Geological Survey.

The color-coded time scale shows the age of different rocks that make up California today.

SEP Analyze Data

✏ Where would you most likely find rocks with no fossils? Look for patterns in the map to identify and circle the location.

The Great Oxidation Event

In order for life to develop on Earth, oxygen was needed in Earth's atmosphere. It took geological and biological changes to kick-start a process (around 2.3 billion years ago) that increased levels of oxygen in the atmosphere. This dramatic rise in atmospheric oxygen is known as "the great oxidation event." The increased supply of atmospheric oxygen led to an explosion in the number and diversity of species. It also made it possible for organisms to adapt to life on land.

Some of the oldest known fossils are around 3.5 billion years old and show the presence of cyanobacteria. These bacteria were unicellular organisms that produced oxygen as a by-product of photosynthesis. Until recently, scientists could not explain why oxygen levels did not increase for another billion years. Research reveals that a rock-forming mineral, olivine, could have been the reason.

Olivine is one of Earth's most abundant minerals. Olivine traps oxygen when it reacts with water. So some scientists have speculated that olivine in the land covered by shallow seas would have absorbed the oxygen that cyanobacteria would have produced. As the composition of Earth's continental surface rocks changed, however, olivine was replaced by other rocks. With less olivine present, oxygen built up in the oceans and atmosphere.

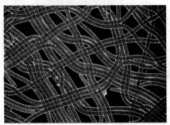

Meet the kick-starters of Earth's atmosphere— olivine (top) and cyanobacteria, better known as blue-green algae (bottom). Rocks with olivine are mined in the Klamath Mountains that run from northern California into Orgeon. Fossils of cyanobacteria can be found in the White-Inyo Mountain range.

Archaeocyatha, a type of ancient sponge, appeared around 530 million years ago. Before going extinct, they evolved into hundreds of different species, many of which were Earth's first reef-builders.

1. **Identify** ✎ Circle the fossil of an Archaeocyatha.
2. **SEP Construct Explanations** Why would reef-building be important for life on Earth and in the ancient land mass that would become California?

....

....

....

Changes in Life Forms

California is rich in fossils. They reveal the amazing variety of species that once lived in California. The fossils reveal how different species have adapted over time as conditions changed. Many animals that once roamed through California now exist only in the form of fossils. The Mojave Desert, for example, contains fossils of ancient horses, ancient elephants, and camels. While many species that once lived in California disappeared from the land mass that become North America, some animals managed to migrate and thrive on other continents.

California's state fossil, the saber-toothed cat (*Smilodon*), was common in California around 2.5 million years ago but went extinct, disappearing around 10,000 years ago. The excavation site at the La Brea Tar Pits in Los Angeles contains many of their fossils, evidence that there was once a sizable population of these ancient cats in California.

All sorts of animals that lived in California during the last Ice Age met their demise in the La Brea Tar Pits: ancient horses, camels, ground sloths, jaguars, mammoths, and saber-toothed cats.

Saber-toothed cats were predators weighing up to 350 kg (770 lbs).

Explain Phenomena What are some environmental conditions that the saber-toothed cat may not have been adapted for that could have caused its extinction?

....

....

....

....

Adapting to Climate Change

Throughout this segment, you will learn about genes and heredity, how organisms adapt to their surroundings, how species change over time, and how scientists are able to understand and order events in Earth's geological history. You will also explore how humans have influenced the evolution of some species on the planet. Understanding these processes helps scientists see how the interrelationships between Earth's systems and processes can affect evolution and the diversity of life. In the topics in this segment, you will investigate the factors that drive evolutionary changes in animals and plants.

A team of scientists, including researchers from the University of California at Riverside, recently discovered a relationship between climate change and evolution. They found that an extreme climate event in the past drastically increased oxygen levels in Earth's ocean-atmosphere system. That event was the thawing of "Snowball Earth." Analyzing trace elements in rocks provided the team with strong evidence for an oxygen spike after a period of thawing. The fossil record further provided evidence of a sudden increase in biodiversity. Because of the thawing, there was an explosion of algae and then small animal life forms.

Snowball Earth refers to a few brief periods 650–900 million years ago when ice covered most of the planet's surface.

Leatherback sea turtles lay their eggs in Indonesia and then swim thousands of miles to their feeding grounds along California's coast. Jellyfish, their main food source, thrive in the upwelling of cooler waters around California.

CCC Stability and Change Consider how a severe climate event that causes water temperatures to increase might affect the leatherback sea turtle.

....

....

....

....

What questions can you ask to help you make sense of this phenomena?

Genes and Heredity

Investigative Phenomenon
How can you use models to describe how changes to genes may affect organisms?

MS-LS3-1 Develop and use a model to describe why structural changes to genes (mutations) located on chromosomes may affect proteins and may result in harmful, beneficial, or neutral effects to the structure and function of the organism.

MS-LS4-4 Construct an explanation based on evidence that describes how genetic variations of traits in a population increase some individuals' probability of surviving and reproducing in a specific environment.

MS-LS4-5 Gather and synthesize information about the technologies that have changed the way humans influence the inheritance of desired traits in organisms.

EP&CIIa Students should be developing an understanding that direct and indirect changes to natural systems due to the growth of human populations and their consumption rates influence the geographic.

EP&CIIc Students should be developing an understanding that the expansion and operation of human communities influences the geographic extent, composition, biological diversity, and viability of natural systems.

How can a black bear family have different colored bears?

What questions do you have about the phenomenon?

① Chromosomes and Inheritance

HANDS-ON LAB

μInvestigate Investigate genetic crosses in imaginary creatures.

MS-LS3-1 Develop and use a model to describe why structural changes to genes (mutations) located on chromosomes may affect proteins and may result in harmful, beneficial, or neutral effects to the structure and function of the organism.

Connect It !

🖊 **Circle the traits that are similar between the parents and the offspring.**

Apply Concepts How were the traits transferred from the parents to the ducklings during reproduction? Where were those traits found?

....

....

....

SEP Construct Explanations Each duckling came from these parents. They look similar, but they are not exactly the same. Why are they not identical? Explain.

....

....

Chromosomes and Genes

Gregor Mendel's ideas about inheritance and probability can be applied to all living things. Mendel determined that traits are inherited using pieces of information that he called factors and we call genes. He observed and experimented with genes in pea plants. He discovered how genes, such as those in ducks (**Figure 1**), were transferred from parents to offspring and how they made certain traits appear. However, Mendel did not know what genes actually look like.

Today, scientists know that genes are segments of code that appear on structures called **chromosomes**. These thread-like **structures** within a cell's nucleus contain DNA that is passed from one generation to the next. The genetic material of chromosomes is condensed and wrapped around special proteins. These provide support for the chromosome structure.

Chromosomes are made in the beginning of the series of events in which a cell grows, prepares for division, and divides into two new cells. During this time, the chromosome gets its characteristic *X* shape.

HANDS-ON LAB

Investigate genetic crosses in imaginary creatures.

Academic Vocabulary

Identify and describe something that has a particular structure.

....

....

....

....

....

Parents Pass Traits to Their Offspring
Figure 1 Each baby mallard duck receives some traits from the mother and some from the father.

Scales of Genetic Material

Figure 2 ✏ Order the structures from smallest to largest by writing the numbers 1 through 5 in the blank circles. Number 1 is the smallest.

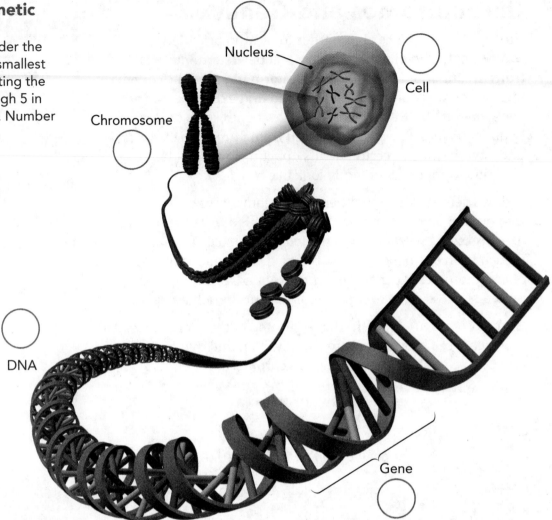

Nucleus

Cell

Chromosome

DNA

Gene

📖 **Make Meaning** Why do sex cells contain only half the number of chromosomes needed for offspring? In your science notebook, explain what would happen if sex cells contained the same number of chromosomes as body cells.

Academic Vocabulary

Your facial features are visible cues to others. They help you express, or show, your emotions. How does this relate to the way genes are expressed?

....

....

....

....

Number of Chromosomes Every cell in your body, other than the sex cells, has the same number of chromosomes. In humans, this number is 46. Other organisms have different numbers of chromosomes, and there is a great variety. For example, mallard ducks have 80 chromosomes. All sexually-reproducing organisms form sex cells, which have half the number of chromosomes that body cells have.

Genes on Chromosomes Every living thing needs instructions to live. Without these instructions, living things would not be able to grow and function. These instructions are located on genes. As you can see in **Figure 2,** genes are located on chromosomes. Genes are **expressed** as traits in organisms, such as hair color.

In humans, between 20,000 and 25,000 genes are found on the 46 chromosomes. Chromosomes are different sizes. Larger chromosomes contain more genes than smaller chromosomes. Each gene contains instructions for coding a particular trait. There are hundreds to thousands of genes coding traits on any given chromosome. For many organisms, these chromosomes come in sets.

Chromosome Pairs During fertilization, you receive 23 chromosomes from your father and 23 chromosomes from your mother. These chromosomes come in pairs, called homologous chromosomes, that contain the same genes. Recall that different forms of a gene are called alleles. Two alleles—one from the mother and one from the father—represent each trait. However, the alleles for these genes may or may not be the same. Some of the alleles for how the gene is expressed may be dominant or recessive. In **Figure 3**, the offspring that received these chromosomes inherited two different forms of some genes—for example, allele *A* from one parent and allele *a* from the other. The individual will be heterozygous for that gene trait. Because more than one gene is present on the 23 pairs of chromosomes, there is a wide variety of allele combinations.

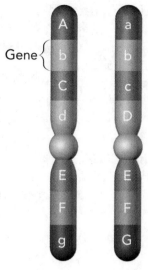

Chromosome pair

A Pair of Chromosomes

Figure 3 🖊 Circle all the pairs of alleles that would be homozygous for a trait.

✅ CHECK POINT **Integrate with Visuals** How would geneticists—people who study genes—know whether the organism in **Figure 3** is homozygous or heterozygous for a certain trait by examining the chromosome pair?

....

....

....

....

Math Toolbox

Counting on Chromosomes

1. **SEP Model with Mathematics** 🖊 Fill in the table with the appropriate chromosome number for the missing body cell or sex cell.

Organisms	Number of Chromosomes	
	Body Cells	Sex Cells
House cat	38	
Mallard duck		40
Corn	20	
Peanut	40	
Horse		32
Oak tree		12
Sweet potato	90	
Camel		35
Chicken	78	

2. **Construct Graphs** 🖊 Complete the line plot below. Place an *X* for each organism whose body cell chromosome number falls within the given range.

Body Cell Chromosome Distribution

```
0–20    21–40    41–60    61–80    81–100
        Number of Chromosomes
```

13

Tracking Traits

Figure 4 ✏ Sickle cell anemia is a recessive genetic disease in humans that changes the structure of red blood cells. In the pedigree, affected members are shaded.

1. **Claim** Circle couples on the pedigree who are clearly both carriers for the trait.

2. **Evidence** What is your proof?

....

....

3. **Reasoning** Explain how your evidence supports your claim.

....

....

....

....

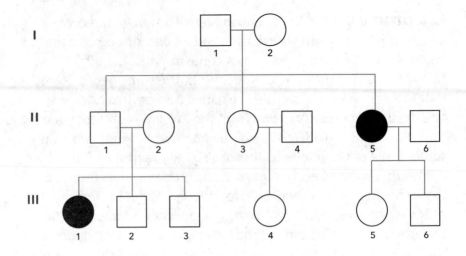

Using a Pedigree

Alelles can sometimes recombine to produce traits that are not favorable, such as a genetic disease. Geneticists study how traits are inherited in order to trace their genetic origin and predict how they may be passed on to future generations.

A pedigree is a model that geneticists use to map out the inheritance of traits. The diagram shows the presence or absence of a trait according to the relationships within a family across several generations. It is like a family tree. **Figure 4** shows multiple generations represented by Roman numerals I, II, and III. Most pedigrees show which family members express a particular trait (shaded figures). Some pedigrees also show the individuals who carry the trait but do not express it (half-shaded figures). In a pedigree, males are represented with squares and females with circles. One horizontal line connects the parent couple and another line leads down from the parents to their children.

Model It !

SEP Develop Models ✏ Think of a trait that you admire. How can that trait get passed through a family? Create a pedigree that outlines the transmission of this trait through a family. Consider who has the trait, who is a carrier for it, and who does not have it.

Forming Sex Cells

In organisms that reproduce sexually, a body cell has twice as many chromosomes as a sex cell. Why is this important? Well, it is through the sex cells that parents pass their genes on to their offspring. When the sperm and egg fuse, they form a zygote, or fertilized egg. The zygote has two sets of chromosomes—one set from the sperm and one set from the egg. Human eggs, for example, contain 23 total chromosomes in a set and sperm contain 23 total chromosomes in a set. So, each of your body cells contains one set of chromosomes from your mother and another set from your father for a total of 46 chromosomes.

Sex cells (sperm and egg) form through a process that reduces the chromosome number by half. It is through this process that homologous chromosomes separate into two different cells. This forms new cells with half as many chromosomes as the parent cell.

Homologous chromosomes have one chromosome from each parent. While the two chromosomes share the same sequence of genes, they may have different alleles. Before the chromosomes separate and move into separate cells, they undergo a process called crossing over. Notice in **Figure 5** that a small segment of one chromosome exchanges places with the corresponding segment on the other chromosome. By exchanging this genetic information, the new cells that form will have a slightly different combination of genes. This allows for minor variations in traits to form, which means there is a higher likelihood that offspring with desirable traits will form within the larger population.

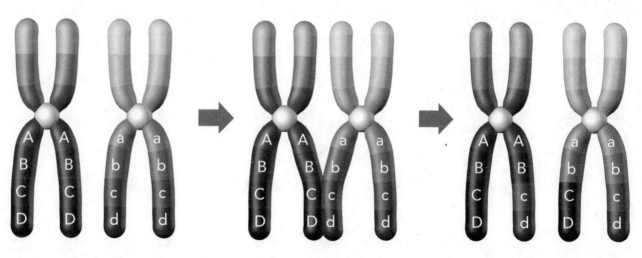

Homologous Chromosomes   Crossing Over   Segments Exchange

MS-LS3-1

Use the pedigree to answer questions 1 & 2.

In humans, free earlobes are dominant and attached earlobes are recessive. The pedigree shows the transmission of attached earlobes through four generations of a family.

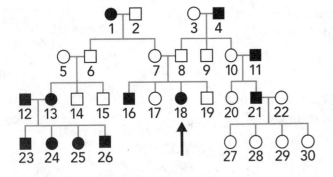

1. SEP Use Models Which male members of the family have attached earlobes?

....

....

2. Predict If the female marked by the arrow (individual 18) has a child with a male carrier, what is the probability their child will have attached earlobes?

....

....

3. SEP Provide Evidence Is chromosome number a good predictor of organism complexity? Explain.

....

....

....

....

....

....

4. SEP Use Mathematics A male king crab has 104 chromosomes in a sperm cell. How many chromosomes does it have in each of its body cells?

....

....

5. CCC Cause and Effect How can crossing over lead to the expression of new traits?

....

....

....

....

....

....

....

....

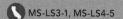

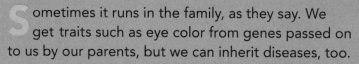

CAREERS

Genetic Counselor

Chromosome
COUNSELORS

Sometimes it runs in the family, as they say. We get traits such as eye color from genes passed on to us by our parents, but we can inherit diseases, too.

Genetic counselors help people who are at risk for a disease or a genetic disorder. They are experts in genetics, so they know better than anyone how genes work. And they are trained counselors, too. They give emotional support and help families make health decisions.

For example, a genetic counselor might help new parents of a baby with Down syndrome. Or the counselor might meet with a patient whose family has a history of Alzheimer's.

Genetic counselors study a family's health history, order genetic tests, and help people to live with a genetic disease. They even advise doctors. They're the genetic experts, and they share their knowledge to help people.

Genetic counselors complete a four-year bachelor's degree in biology or a healthcare field. After graduating, they work on completing a master's degree. This degree will focus on human genetics and counseling. They also complete extensive research. In addition, excellent communication and decision-making skills are required.

▶ VIDEO

Watch what's involved with being a genetic counselor.

📄 DOCUMENT

Go online to explore more science and engineering careers.

MY CAREER

Want to help people understand their genes? Do an online search for "genetic counselor" to learn more about this career.

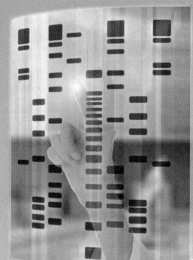

Phenomenon Genetic counselors help others understand the complex world of DNA, genes, and chromosomes.

② Trait Variations

MS-LS3-1 Develop and use a model to describe why structural changes to genes (mutations) located on chromosomes may affect proteins and may result in harmful, beneficial, or neutral effects to the structure and function of the organism.

MS-LS4-4 Construct an explanation based on evidence that describes how genetic variations of traits in a population increase some individuals' probability of surviving and reproducing in a specific environment. (Also **EP&CIIc**)

Connect It!

✏️ **Circle a trait that distinguishes the male elephant seal from the female.**

Determine Differences What other differences do you notice between the male and female elephant seals?

....

....

CCC Structure and Function What traits allow the elephant seal to live in water? Explain your reasoning.

....

....

....

Diversity of Life

Organisms that are the same species tend to have many similarities. The Northern elephant seals in **Figure 1**, however, show that very different traits can exist in two individuals. Some differences are visible traits, such as wrinkled skin or brown hair. Others are invisible, such as type I diabetes or sickle-cell anemia in humans. Differences have the potential to be passed on from one generation to the next, and change the population.

The diversity of life on Earth relies in part on the variety of traits within a species. Any difference between individuals of the same species is a **variation**. Two friends with different eye color have a variation (green, brown) of the same trait (eye color). Variations may be due to DNA inherited from the parents, exposure to certain environmental factors, or a combination of both inheritance and environmental factors.

Variations can be helpful, harmful, or neutral. Consider a population of butterflies avoiding predators. Some have the same wing color pattern as a poisonous species. When this variation is passed from one generation to the next, the offspring are more likely to survive and reproduce. A harmful variation, on the other hand, threatens a population's survival. For example, low blood oxygen levels can be found in people with sickle-cell anemia. Neutral variations, such as different eye color, do not benefit or harm the population.

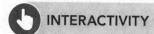

INTERACTIVITY

Identify traits found on a dog.

Northern Elephant Seals

Figure 1 These Northern elephant seals—two bellowing males and several females—relax on a beach near San Simeon. Although these seals are the same species and share most of the same DNA, there are differences in their appearances.

Chromosomes and Variation

You received 23 chromosomes from your mother and 23 chromosomes from your father. The combination of genes found on these chromosomes codes for the proteins that determine your traits.

Types of Chromosomes There are two types of chromosomes found in every one of your cells. Of the 23 pairs of chromosomes, one pair is sex chromosomes, while the other 22 pairs are autosomal chromosomes. **Sex chromosomes** are the pair of chromosomes carrying genes that determine whether a person is biologically male or female.

The combination of sex chromosomes determines the sex of the offspring. A human female inherits one X chromosome from her mother and one X chromosome from her father. A male receives one X chromosome from his mother and one Y chromosome from his father. **Figure 2** compares the X and Y chromosomes.

The 22 pairs of chromosomes that are not sex chromosomes are **autosomal chromosomes**. You inherit half of your autosomal chromosomes from your mother and half from your father. All the pairs of autosomal chromosomes are homologous chromosomes. This means that the genes for a trait are located at the same place on each chromosome in the pair, even though the alleles may be different. Females also have homologous sex chromosomes, while males do not.

INTERACTIVITY

Explore how some genetic disorders are carried on sex chromosomes.

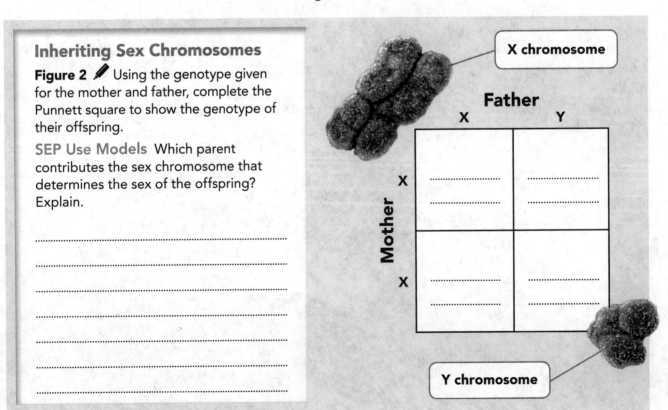

Inheriting Sex Chromosomes

Figure 2 🖊 Using the genotype given for the mother and father, complete the Punnett square to show the genotype of their offspring.

SEP Use Models Which parent contributes the sex chromosome that determines the sex of the offspring? Explain.

....

....

....

....

....

....

....

X chromosome

Father

X   Y

Mother

X

X

Y chromosome

Chromosome Size

Chromosomes contain DNA, and each section of DNA that codes for a protein is a gene. DNA is made of small pieces called nitrogen bases. There are four different kinds of nitrogen bases, which always pair according to the same rules to form base pairs. For every trait, there is a gene or group of genes that controls the trait by producing proteins through the process of protein synthesis. Because the number of genes found on each chromosome and the length of each gene varies, chromosomes come in different sizes. For example, the X chromosome is almost three times the size of the Y chromosome and contains close to 16 times as many genes. Thus, it codes for more proteins, and determines more traits.

✅ CHECK POINT **Cite Textual Evidence** Why does the X chromosome express more traits than the Y chromosome?

....

Chromosome and Gene Relationship

This data shows chromosome size as number of base pairs in the millions (Mbp) and estimated number of genes found on each one.

1. **Construct a Scatter Plot** 🖊 Complete the scatter plot. Each dot represents the relationship between the total base pairs and the estimated number of genes for each chromosome.

Human Chromosome Size vs. Number of Genes

Estimated Number of Genes (y-axis: 0 to 2,000)
Millions of Base Pairs (Mbp) (x-axis: 0 to 250)

Chromosome	Mbp	Genes
1	248.96	2000
2	242.19	1300
3	198.3	1000
4	190.22	1000
5	181.54	900
6	170.81	1000
7	159.35	900
8	145.14	700
9	138.4	800
10	133.8	700
11	135.09	1300
12	133.28	1100
13	114.36	300
14	107.04	800
15	101.99	600
16	90.34	800
17	83.26	1200
18	80.37	200
19	58.62	1500
20	64.44	500
21	46.71	200
22	50.82	500
X	156.04	800
Y	57.23	50

2. **SEP Interpret Data** What relationship do you see between chromosome size and number of genes?

....

....

Types of Mutations

An organism can develop traits due to changes in its genetic code. A **mutation** is any change in the DNA of a gene or chromosome. A mutation can cause an organism's trait to be different than what it normally would be. Mutations can be inherited from a parent or acquired during an organism's life. Inherited mutations occur when the parent passes on the mutation during reproduction. These mutations are present throughout the life of the organism, and are in every cell of the body. Acquired mutations occur at some point during an organism's lifetime. Acquired mutations can only be passed on from parent to offspring if the mutations occur in sex cells.

Genetic Mutations Many mutations are the result of small changes in the organism's DNA. Just one small change to an organism's genetic information is a mutation and may cause an incorrect protein to be made. As a result, the trait may be different from what was expressed before. **Figure 3** shows genetic mutations that can result when genetic information is deleted, added, or substituted.

Sex-Linked Mutations A mutation can occur on any chromosome. Some mutations occur on **sex-linked genes**, which are genes carried on a sex chromosome. Because the X chromosome has more genes than the Y chromosome, most sex-linked mutations occur on the X chromosome. In addition, many sex-linked mutations are recessive. Hemophilia is a recessive sex-linked mutation, where the individual's ability to clot blood is reduced. Males are more likely to exhibit hemophilia because they have only one X chromosome.

Genetic Mutations

Figure 3 The diagram shows three types of mutations.

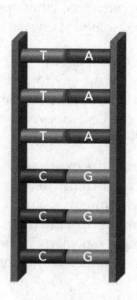

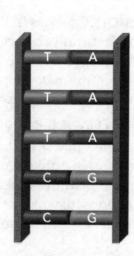

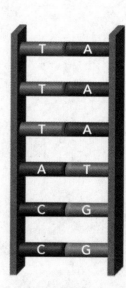

Original DNA sequence

Deletion: one base pair is removed.

Addition: one base pair is added.

Substitution: one base pair is switched for another.

VIDEO

Investigate how mutations
can affect organisms.

Environmental Factors

Interactions with our surroundings and the conditions in which we live have the potential to change the way genes are normally expressed. First, environmental factors can change an organism's genetic makeup. Secondly, the chemicals found on DNA can be changed.

Organisms encounter harmful chemicals and radiation on a regular basis. These agents are called mutagens because they can damage DNA in such way that it causes mutations. Some mutagens naturally occur, while others are synthetic. For example, radiation in the form of ultraviolet (UV) or X-rays are naturally occurring mutagens. Synthetic mutagens can be found in pesticides, asbestos, and food additives introduced by expanding human communities. Human introduced mutagens have the potential to negatively influence biological diversity.

Gene Expression Changes in the way genes are expressed may occur naturally or because of the environment. An example of natural change is when a caterpillar transitions to a butterfly. As the organism develops, the DNA does not change, but the genes are read and expressed differently.

The environment can change the way genes are expressed. Identical twins have the same DNA, but can acquire different traits when they grow up in different environments. Activities such as smoking and unhealthy eating habits can also alter the way genes are expressed, which changes a person's traits. **Figure 4** shows another way genes can be expressed differently.

Damage from Sun Exposure

Figure 4 ✏ UV radiation from the sun harms skin cells. UVA radiation penetrates into the deep layers of the skin and can alter skin structure. UVB radiation penetrates only the top layer of the skin. Draw arrows in the first diagram to show how deep UVA and UVB penetrate into the skin. Then, identify the radiation type—UVA or UVB—in the box next to the picture that shows a possible effect of the radiation.

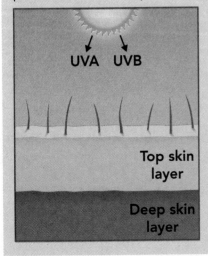

UVA   UVB

Top skin
layer

Deep skin
layer

Camouflage
Figure 5 ✏ Sometimes mutations benefit the survival of a species. Predators will likely not see this animal, passing it as they swim. Circle the leopard flounder fish that is camouflaged.

Mutation Effects
Mutations may be harmful, helpful, or neutral. Helpful mutations are those that benefit the survival of the species and are often passed on to offspring. Harmful mutations do not benefit the species and often decrease the likelihood of survival. Neutral mutations are those that do not affect an organism's chance of survival.

Helpful Mutations Some mutations can help an organism survive in their environment. One example of a helpful mutation is camouflage, which is the ability to blend in with the environment. In **Figure 5**, camouflage protects an organism from predators that may be looking for a meal. In humans, a mutation in a gene controlling fast-twitch muscles produces sprinters who are world-class athletes.

Harmful Mutations Genetic disorders and cancer are both the result of harmful mutations. A genetic disorder is an abnormal condition that a person inherits through genes or chromosomes. Cystic fibrosis is a genetic disorder that causes the body to make thick mucus in the lungs and digestive system. The mucus builds up in the lungs and blocks air flow. Cancer is a disease in which some body cells grow and divide uncontrollably, damaging the parts of the body around them. Few cancers are inherited. Most cancers are caused by acquired mutations that occur from damage to genes during the life of an organism.

Neutral Mutations Not all mutations are helpful or harmful. Some mutations, such as human hair color, may be neutral and have no impact on the survival of an organism. There may also be mutations that still code for the same protein. Even though the DNA sequence has changed, the amino acid that is produced remains the same.

☑ CHECK POINT **Distinguish Facts** In what ways can the environment impact the traits of an organism?

....

....

....

Mutations in Reproduction

Not all mutations are the result of small changes in the DNA in an organism's body cells. Some mutations occur when chromosomes do not separate correctly during the formation of sex cells. When this happens, a sex cell can end up with too many or too few chromosomes. When a chromosomal mutation occurs, either additional proteins are created or fewer proteins are created.

Protein Changes Amino acids are the building blocks of proteins, which can be considered the architects of cell function. A change in the amino acid sequence can alter the final protein. The result is a mutation, which may or may not be detectable.

Some genes move to a new location on the genome. The movement could lead to a mutation due to changes in instructions to make the protein. Or, the instructions could remain intact, but now they are in a different place on the genome. Scientists are trying to understand the purpose of these 'jumping genes'. Sometimes they jump to a location that disrupts a functioning gene. When this occurs, the gene is not able to express itself, which can cause traits to change. Scientists speculate that jumping genes may cause a species to change. Scientists have also recently discovered that some species of octopus and squid, such as the one shown in **Figure 6**, are able to make specific proteins in response to a changing environment.

Changing RNA

Figure 6 Some organisms, such as this squid, can produce different proteins in response to a changing environment.

Synthesize Information Why is it beneficial for scientists to understand how other organisms are able to edit which proteins are created?

....

....

....

....

MS-LS3-1, MS-LS4-4, EP&CIIc

1. SEP Communicate Information How can mutations change an organism's traits?

....

....

....

....

....

....

....

2. SEP Construct Explanations How is an organism's ability to produce offspring affected by changes to a chromosome?

....

....

....

....

....

....

3. Evaluate Claims A student states that only a male human offspring can express a recessive sex-linked X chromosome mutation. Is this statement accurate? Explain.

....

....

....

....

....

....

....

4. Connect to the Environment A scientist observes that members of a fish species near a popular beach had more acquired mutations than the same species in a river. Form a hypothesis stating how this difference could affect the future of the species.

....

....

....

....

....

....

....

....

....

5. SEP Construct an Argument If a baker making chocolate chip cookies accidentally misreads a recipe and adds something extra, forgets to add something, or adds the wrong ingredient, what can happen to the cookies? Explain how this analogy can be used to describe a mutation.

....

....

....

....

....

....

....

....

....

....

....

LESSON 3 Genetic Technologies

HANDS-ON LAB

µInvestigate Extract DNA from a strawberry.

MS-LS4-5 Gather and synthesize information about the technologies that have changed the way humans influence the inheritance of desired traits in organisms.

Connect It !

🖋 **Dogs come in many different shapes, sizes, and colors. Which of the ones shown here would you prefer as a pet? Circle your choice.**

CCC Cause and Effect Many purebred dogs have problems later in life, such as joint or eye diseases. Why are purebred dogs more likely to develop problems later in life?

....

....

Make Inferences What can be done to decrease the likelihood of these problems appearing?

....

....

Artificial Selection

When consumers make choices, they are often attracted to products with the highest quality. We want the healthiest and best-tasting fruits and vegetables. We want the right amount of fat and flavor in our meats. We even want the best traits in our pets, such as the dogs you see in **Figure 1**. These high-quality products do not appear only in nature. Scientists and breeders have influenced the traits that other organisms inherit through the process of selective breeding.

Selective Breeding In the natural world, individuals with beneficial traits are more likely to survive and successfully reproduce than individuals without those traits. This is called natural selection. **Artificial selection** is also known as selective breeding. It occurs when humans breed only those organisms with desired traits to produce the next generation. It's important to note that desired traits are not necessarily the traits that benefit the organism's chances for survival. Instead, they are traits that humans desire.

Dogs, cats, and livestock animals have all been selectively bred. Cows, chickens, and pigs have been bred to be larger so that they produce more milk or meat. Breeding and caring for farm animals that have certain genetic traits that humans desire is called animal husbandry. The many different breeds of dogs shown in **Figure 1** have also been bred over time for very specific functions.

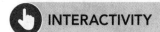

INTERACTIVITY

Take a poll about genetic modification in food.

Literacy Connection

Corroborate Find statements in the text that support the claim that artificial selection is not a natural process and does not necessarily help the organism's survival.

Purebred Dogs

Figure 1 Each type of purebred dog shown here is the result of selective breeding over the course of many generations.

Genetic Engineering

With the discovery of DNA and its relationship to genes, scientists have developed more methods to produce desired traits. Through a process called **genetic engineering**, modern geneticists can transfer a gene from the DNA of one organism into another. Genetic engineering is used to give organisms genes they could not acquire through breeding.

Scientists use genetic engineering techniques to insert specific desired genes into animals. By **manipulating** a gene, scientists have created a fish that glows when under a black light **(Figure 2)**. A jellyfish gene for fluorescence was inserted into a fertilized fish egg to produce the glowing fish. Scientists are hoping that further research on this gene will lead to a method that helps track toxic chemicals in the body.

Genetic engineering is also used to synthesize materials. A protein hormone called insulin helps control blood-sugar levels after eating. People who have diabetes cannot effectively control their blood-sugar levels, and many must take insulin injections. Prior to 1980, some diabetics were injecting themselves with insulin from other animals without getting the desired results. To help diabetics, scientists genetically engineered bacteria to produce the first human protein— insulin. The process they used, and still use today, is shown in **Figure 3**. Furthermore, bacteria can reproduce quickly, so large amounts of human insulin are produced in a short time.

Glowing Fish

Figure 2 Genetic engineering made glowing fish possible.

Academic Vocabulary

Explain the difference between manipulating a tool and manipulating another person.

....

....

....

....

....

....

....

Plan It!

Synthesize a New Trait

✎ Create a trait that has never been seen before in an animal. Identify a trait you would like an animal to have. Then, sketch the animal and describe a process by which you could achieve your desired result.

....

....

....

....

....

....

....

Bacteria Make Human Insulin

Figure 3 ✏ Bacteria can be used to produce insulin in humans. Complete the diagram by showing the process for Step 5.

HANDS-ON LAB

Investigate Extract DNA from a strawberry.

❶ Small rings of DNA, or plasmids, are found in some bacteria cells.

❷ Scientists remove the plasmid and cut it open with an enzyme. They then insert an insulin gene that has been removed from human DNA.

❸ The human insulin gene attaches to the open ends of the plasmid to form a closed ring.

❹ Some bacteria cells take up the plasmids that have the insulin gene.

❺ When the cells reproduce, the new cells contain copies of the "engineered" plasmid. The foreign gene directs the cells to produce human insulin.

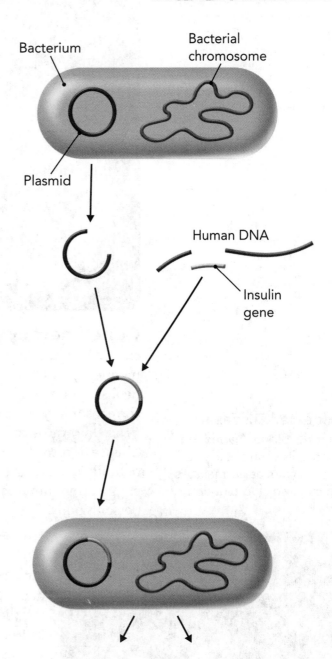

31

T-cell Destroys Cancer Cell

Figure 4 T-cells are a type of white blood cell that help to fight disease in your body. Scientists have genetically engineered a T-cell that can attack and destroy up to 1,000 cancer cells.

Predict How might doctors use this new T-cell?

....

....

....

....

....

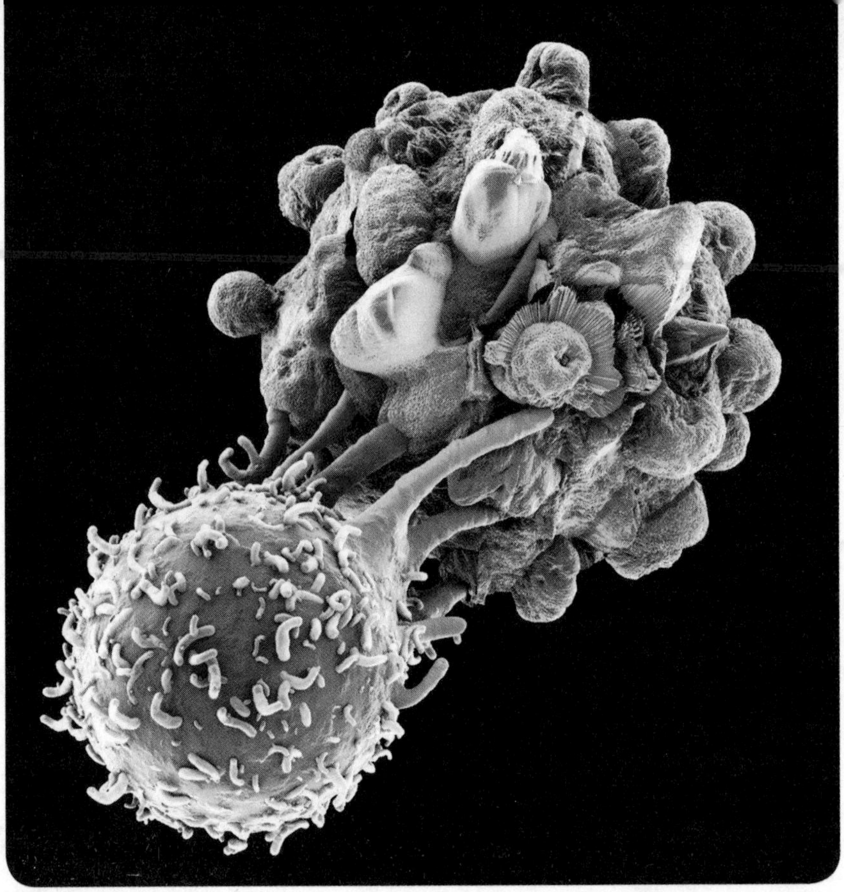

Sickle-cell Disease

Figure 5 Sickle-shaped red blood cells cannot carry as much oxygen as normal cells and can also clog blood vessels.

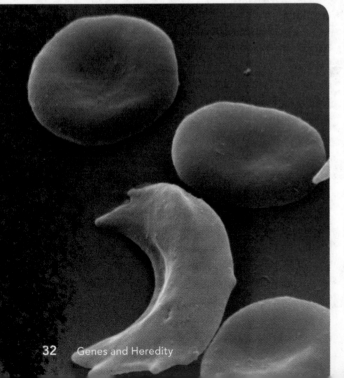

Gene Therapy in Humans

Genetic diseases are caused by mutations, or changes in the DNA code. Some mutated genes pass from parent to child; others occur spontaneously. Soon, it may be possible to use genetic engineering to correct some genetic disorders in humans. This process, called **gene therapy**, involves changing a gene to treat a medical disease or disorder. A normal working gene replaces an absent or faulty gene. One promising therapy involves genetically engineering immune-system cells and injecting them into a person's body.

Millions of people worldwide suffer from sickle cell disease. This painful genetic disorder is caused by a single mutation that affects hemoglobin, a protein in red blood cells. Hemoglobin carries oxygen. The mutation causes the blood cells to be shaped like a sickle, or crescent, as shown in **Figure 5.**

CRISPR is a gene-editing tool that can potentially help people with sickle cell disease. CRISPR uses a "guide RNA" and an enzyme to cut out the DNA sequence causing the dangerous mutation. The "guide RNA" takes the enzyme to the DNA sequence with the sickle cell mutation, and the enzyme then removes that sequence. Then another tool pastes a copy of the normal sequence into the DNA.

Cloning Organisms A **clone** is an organism that has the same genes as the organism from which it was produced. The process of cloning involves removing an unfertilized egg and replacing its nucleus with the nucleus of a body cell from the same species. Because this body cell has a full set of chromosomes, the offspring will have the same DNA as the individual that donated the body cell. The egg is then implanted into a female so it can develop. If the process is successful, the clone is born.

Cloning is used to develop many of the foods we eat. Many plants are cloned simply by taking a small piece of the original and putting it in suitable conditions to grow. For example, the Cavendish banana (see **Figure 6**) is the most common banana for eating. All these bananas are clones of the original plant. Cloning helps to produce crops of consistent quality. But a population with little genetic diversity has drawbacks, both for farmers and for people who rely on the crop for food.

☑CHECK POINT **Summarize Text** List the steps in creating a clone.

....

....

....

....

▶ VIDEO

Learn how selective breeding and cloning can lead to populations with desired traits.

📓 **Write About It**
Cloning food crops has many advantages. Every commercial banana crop, worldwide, is cloned. Write about how a disease that destroyed the Cavendish banana could affect society. Consider farmers, fruit companies, grocery stores, everyday people, and others who would be affected.

Cloned Bananas
Figure 6 A fungus that causes bananas to rot is spreading across the globe. The Cavendish banana is particularly vulnerable.

SEP Construct Explanations
Why is a disease more damaging to cloned crops?

....

....

....

....

....

....

Genetic Cousins
Figure 7 Humans and modern-day chimpanzees share about 99 percent of their DNA.

Infer How does knowing we are close genetically to chimpanzees help humans?

....

....

....

....

....

INTERACTIVITY

Gather fingerprints and identify who committed a crime.

Practical Uses for DNA

Due to new technologies, geneticists now study and use genes in ways that weren't possible before. Modern geneticists can now determine the exact sequence of nitrogen bases in an organism's DNA. This process is called DNA sequencing.

Sequencing the Human Genome Breaking a code with six billion letters may seem like an impossible task to undertake. But scientists working on the Human Genome Project did just that. The complete set of genetic information that an organism carries in its DNA is called a **genome**. The main goal of the Human Genome Project was to identify the DNA sequence of the entire human genome. Since sequencing the human genome, scientists now research the functions of tens of thousands of human genes. Some of these genes also allow scientists to better understand certain diseases.

Our genome can also help us understand how humans evolved on Earth. All life on Earth evolved from simple, single-celled organisms that lived billions of years ago, and we still have evidence of this in our DNA. For example, there are some genes that exist in the cells of almost every organism on Earth, which suggests we all evolved from a common ancestor. Some organisms share a closer relationship than others. By comparing genomes of organisms, scientists continue to piece together a history of how life on Earth evolved.

DNA Technologies Before the Human Genome Project, scientists such as Gregor Mendel used experimentation to understand heredity. Since the project's completion in 2003, the use of technologies to understand heredity and how DNA guides life processes has increased greatly. For example, DNA technologies help diagnose genetic diseases.

Genetic disorders typically result from one or more changed genes, called mutations. Medical specialists can carry out a DNA screening to detect the presence of a mutation. To complete a DNA screen, samples of DNA are analyzed for the presence of one or more mutated genes. This information is then used to help those individuals whose DNA includes mutated genes.

DNA comparisons determine how closely related you are to another person. To do this, DNA from a person's cell is broken down into small pieces, or fragments. These fragments are put into a machine that separates them by size. When this happens, a pattern is produced creating a DNA fingerprint, like the one shown in **Figure 8**. Similarities between patterns determine who contributed the DNA. Genetic fingerprints can be used to tie a person to a crime scene, prevent the wrong person from going to jail, identify remains, or identify the father of a child.

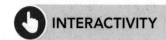

INTERACTIVITY

Consider using technology to solve the world's food problem.

DNA Fingerprint

Figure 8 Circle the suspect that left his or her DNA at the crime scene.

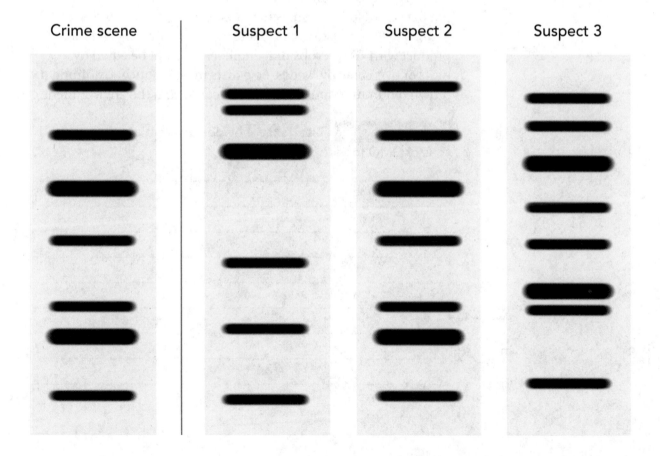

Crime scene | Suspect 1 | Suspect 2 | Suspect 3

Controversies of DNA Use

As genetic research advances, some people are concerned about how genetic information will be used or altered. Some people are concerned about who can access their DNA information, and how this information will be used.

Your genetic information is the only truly unique part of your identity, and many people want to keep it as private as possible. The Genetic Information Nondiscrimination Act (GINA) was signed into law in 2008. This act makes it illegal for health insurance companies and employers to discriminate against individuals based on genetic information. Health insurance companies cannot deny you care, and a company cannot refuse to hire you simply because of the results of a genetic test (**Figure 9**). Your genetic information cannot be used without your consent, and it must be used in a way that is fair and just.

Some people are concerned about the use of genetically modified organisms (GMOs) in the food supply. GMOs are made by changing DNA so desired traits are expressed. Growing our food from seeds that have been genetically modified is controversial. Many people fear the impact it could have on human health and the environment in the future. One concern is that DNA from GMOs could mix with DNA from wild organisms when they reproduce. This might introduce traits into a population that are not beneficial for survival, since GMOs are usually engineered to grow faster or taste better. Yet farmers are able to yield more product with GMO crops that engineered to not be eaten by pests or overcome by weeds. Scientists must balance sustaining a growing human population with safeguarding the environment.

✅ CHECK POINT **Cite Textual Evidence** What are the pros and cons of GMO foods?

....

....

....

....

....

....

....

....

....

Using Genetic Information

Figure 9 Some people fear that medical insurance companies will not cover their medical expenses if they have been genetically tested and results show a genetic disorder.

Evaluate Reasoning Why is this a fear of many people? What can we do to protect our privacy?

....

....

....

....

....

....

....

....

....

....

☑LESSON 3 Check

1. **Identify** Shortly after World War II, chickens were bred to grow much more quickly and to produce much more meat. Which process is this an example of?

....

2. **Compare and Contrast** What are some positive and negative ways that genetic information may be used?

....

....

....

3. **CCC Cause and Effect** Some genetically engineered organisms can mate with wild members of their species. Farmed fish are often genetically modified. What can happen to wild fish of their species if mating occurs?

....

....

....

4. **SEP Construct Explanations** Gorillas and humans evolved from a common ancestor. Geneticists found that they may be more closely related than previously thought. How can DNA sequencing of the gorilla and human genomes determine this?

....

....

....

....

5. **SEP Evaluate Information** A classmate states that animals that result from artificial selection are "lucky," since they have better traits than naturally bred animals. Given your study of this topic, do you agree? Explain.

....

....

....

....

....

6. **CCC Relate Structure and Function** How can changes to the structure of DNA lead to the development of new traits in a species?

....

....

....

....

....

....

....

....

....

....

....

7. **SEP Design Solutions** The procedure used to make insulin in bacteria can also be used to synthesize other biological materials. Think of a chemical or material inside the human body that might be synthesized within bacteria. What would be the potential benefits of this process? What would be the potential drawbacks?

....

....

....

....

....

....

....

....

....

....

....

....

MS-LS4-5

REINVENTING DNA AS Data Storage

 VIDEO

Discover how scientists use DNA to solve data storage problems.

How much digital space

do you need for all your texts, emails, photos, and music? Digital information can take up lots of space.

Code	P	l	a	y
Binary data	01010000	01101100	01100001	01111001
DNA nucleotides	GCGAG	ATCGA	AGAGC	TGCTCT

The Challenge: To provide storage solutions for the data storage needs of everyone on Earth.

Phenomenon Some estimates state that the world has 40 trillion gigabytes (GB) of data. Forty trillion GB equals about 40 million petabytes (PB). Ten billion photos on social media sites use about 1.5 PB. So, if every star in our Milky Way galaxy were one byte of data, then we would need 5,000 Milky Ways, each with 200 billion stars, to amass one PB of data. How can we possibly store all of our data?

Science may offer an answer: DNA. Our entire genetic code fits within the nucleus of a single cell. Scientists have figured out how to convert digital data (in 1s and 0s) into DNA's A-C-T-G code. Then they constructed synthetic DNA in a lab. So far, scientists have been able to encode and store images and videos within a single strand of DNA. If current cost constraints are overcome, DNA could be the next microchip. Someday, the data currently stored on computers in enormous buildings may fit in the palm of your hand!

Science may solve the engineering problem of our exploding data storage needs. Scientists can store documents and photos by converting digital code to DNA code and then making synthetic DNA. To retrieve a file, the DNA code gets converted back to digital code.

DESIGN CHALLENGE Can you design your own code to store information? Go to the Engineering Design Notebook to find out!

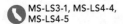

MS-LS3-1, MS-LS4-4,
MS-LS4-5

Evidence-Based Assessment

Scientists have figured out a way to insert the genes of one organism into another. A genetically modified organism, GMO, expresses, or shows, desired traits that prove to be beneficial to many farmers. Reliance on GMO crops has been increasing in the United States for many years.

The graph shows three genetically modified crops—corn, soybeans, and cotton. In each crop, the DNA has been engineered for a desired trait. New DNA sequences that code for specific proteins are inserted into a crop's DNA.

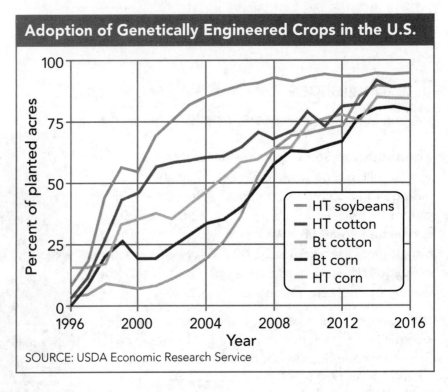

Adoption of Genetically Engineered Crops in the U.S.

SOURCE: USDA Economic Research Service

For example, some crops have been engineered to resist droughts. The gene for drought resistance is cut from the DNA of a desert-dwelling species and then inserted into the crop species. The resistance-to-drought trait will be expressed when these genetically engineered crop plants reproduce. In the graph, you can observe data on another desirable trait that has been produced through genetic engineering is improved herbicide tolerance (HT). This trait protects the GMO crop when herbicides are sprayed on the fields to kill weeds. The Bt crop includes a gene from the *Bacillus thuringiensis* bacterium. This gene produces a protein that kills the larvae of the corn borer, a pest. Farmers can grow Bt crops instead of spraying insecticides that could also kill helpful insects, such as bees.

1. SEP Analyze Data Which genetically engineered crop has shown the greatest increase in usage from 2006 to 2016?
A. HT Corn
B. Bt Corn
C. HT Cotton
D. HT Soybeans

2. CCC Patterns What patterns do you observe in the line graphs for the crops that are herbicide tolerant, HT? Support your claim.

....
....
....
....
....
....
....
....
....
....
....
....
....
....
....
....
....

3. Connect to the Environment Which statement is true about GMO crops?
☐ GMOs reduce the need for chemical pesticides.

☐ Years of research confirm that GMOs are safe for human consumption.

☐ GMOs increase the need for chemical pesticides.

4. CCC Stability and Change Each box below contains an idea about why genetically engineered crops may be used in the future. Sequence the boxes to infer how the ideas would be used in a flowchart.

| GMO crops now account for most acres of farm land. | _____ |

| Use of GMOs has been increasing for ten years. | _____ |

| This trend will continue because it saves time and money. | _____ |

MS-LS3-1

Modeling Mutations

How can you use a **model** to show how **mutations** work?

Background

Phenomenon You have observed the phenomenon of mutations whether you have realized it or not. A fruit or vegetable in a grocery store that is not quite the right color or shape, or an animal that has discolored fur, hair, or skin might be expressing genetic mutations.

We can use models to show what a mutation is. Small mutations in genes can result in changes to proteins. These changes can affect the structures and functions of the organism. Mutations can have a positive, negative, or neutral effect on an organism.

Materials

Paper and pencil

HANDS-ON LAB

uDemonstrate Go online for a downloadable worksheet for this lab.

Design Your Investigation

1. Think of a short word.
2. Write the word here.

....

Procedure

3. Write a code for a mutation.
4. Write 3 new codes for 3 more mutations from the previous mutation.
5. Diagram your word model below and identify what the mutation was.

Develop Your Model

Analyze and Interpret Data

1. **SEP Develop a Model** How did each mutation affect your word?

....
....
....
....
....

2. **SEP Analyze Data** How would you categorize the changes?

....
....
....
....
....

3. **SEP Use a Model to Evaluate** How does your model represent a mutation?

....
....
....
....
....

4. **CCC Cause and Effect** How can mutations affect organisms? Provide an example.

....
....
....
....

Natural Selection and Change Over Time

Investigative Phenomenon

What kinds of data and evidence explain how characteristics of organisms change over time?

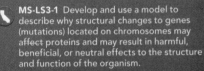

MS-LS3-1 Develop and use a model to describe why structural changes to genes (mutations) located on chromosomes may affect proteins and may result in harmful, beneficial, or neutral effects to the structure and function of the organism.

MS-LS4-1 Analyze and interpret data for patterns in the fossil record that document the existence, diversity, extinction, and change of life forms throughout the history of life on Earth under the assumption that natural laws operate today as in the past.

MS-LS4-2 Apply scientific ideas to construct an explanation for the anatomical similarities and differences among modern organisms and between modern and fossil organisms to infer evolutionary relationships.

MS-LS4-3 Analyze displays of pictorial data to compare patterns of similarities in the embryological development across multiple species to identify relationships not evident in the fully formed anatomy.

MS-LS4-4 Construct an explanation based on evidence that describes how genetic variations of traits in a population increase some individuals' probability of surviving and reproducing in a specific environment.

MS-LS4-5 Gather and synthesize information about the technologies that have changed the way humans influence the inheritance of desired traits in organisms.

MS-LS4-6 Use mathematical representations to support explanations of how natural selection may lead to increases and decreases of specific traits in populations over time.

EP&CIIa Students should be developing an understanding that the direct and indirect changes to natural systems due to the growth of human populations and their consumption rates influence the geographic extent, composition, biological diversity, and viability of natural systems.

EP&CIIc Students should be developing an understanding that the expansion and operation of human communities influences the geographic extent, composition, biological diversity, and viability of natural systems.

Has this dragonfly changed from its fossilized ancestor?

HANDS-ON LAB

□**Connect** Analyze evidence that whales may have walked on land.

What questions do you have about the phenomenon?

....
....
....
....
....
....
....
....
....
....

Quest PBL

A Migration Puzzle

Figure It Out To understand how bird populations change over time in response to environmental conditions, ornithologists (scientists who study birds) analyze long-term data. In this problem-based Quest activity, you will investigate factors that may be influencing changes in two populations of European blackcaps. By applying what you learn from each lesson, digital activity, and hands-on lab, you will determine what is causing the changes to the bird populations. Then in the Findings activity, you will prepare a multimedia report to communicate what you have learned and to explain the changes in the blackcap populations.

NBC LEARN ▶ VIDEO

After watching the Quest Kickoff video about migrating golden eagles, list some of the factors that might affect the birds' migration patterns and routes.

....

....

....

....

....

....

....

....

👆 **INTERACTIVITY**

A Migration Puzzle

MS-LS3-1, MS-LS4-1, MS-LS4-2, MS-LS4-4, MS-LS4-5, MS-LS4-6, EP&CIIa, EP&CIIc

---

Quest CHECK-IN

IN LESSON 1
What differences exist between the UK and Spanish blackcaps? Determine evidence for variations in the European blackcap populations.

👆 **INTERACTIVITY**

Meet the Blackcaps

IN LESSON 2
What are the roles of genes and mutations in natural selection? Think about how you can include these factors in your report.

Quest CHECK-IN

IN LESSON 3
How can natural selection and inherited variations influence a population? Investigate factors that may have caused the variations in the European blackcaps.

👆 **INTERACTIVITY**

Evolution of the Blackcaps

In the 1960s, some European blackcaps started migrating to the United Kingdom from Central Europe during the winter. Over time, they have formed a distinct population of blackcaps.

IN LESSON 4

What can you learn from the fossil record? Think about how the fossil record of the European blackcap might provide information on how the bird has adapted over time.

Quest CHECK-IN

IN LESSON 5

What else would be helpful to know about European blackcaps? Research your questions and gather information to include in your report.

👆 INTERACTIVITY

Prepare Your Report

Quest FINDINGS

Complete the Quest!

Create a multimedia report about the two populations of European blackcaps and what caused them to be so different from each other.

👆 INTERACTIVITY

Reflect on Blackcap Migration

Early Study of Evolution

HANDS-ON LAB

ωInvestigate Model how species change over time.

MS-LS4-4 Construct an explanation based on evidence that describes how genetic variations of traits in a population increase some individuals' probability of surviving and reproducing in a specific environment.

Connect It

✏️ **Draw an arrow pointing to the squirrel that you think is better suited for the environment.**

SEP Construct Explanations Why do you think that squirrel is better suited for the environment? Explain your reasoning.

....

....

....

....

Observing Changes

Suppose you put a birdfeeder outside your kitchen or classroom window. You enjoy watching birds and gray squirrels come to get a free meal. The squirrels seem to be perfectly skilled at climbing the feeder and breaking open seeds. One day, you are surprised to see a white squirrel, like the squirrel in **Figure 1**, visiting the feeder. This new white squirrel and the gray squirrel appear to be the same **species**—a group of similar organisms that can mate with each other and produce offspring that can also mate and reproduce. You would probably have a few questions about where this squirrel came from and why it is white!

Curiosity About How Life Changes Scientists such as Charles Darwin were also curious about the differences they observed in natural populations. A variation is any difference between individuals of the same species. Some scientists asked how life on Earth got started and how it has changed over time throughout the planet's history. The scientists wondered what dinosaurs were like and why they disappeared. Darwin and others worked to develop a theory of **evolution**—the process by which modern organisms have descended from ancient organisms.

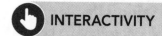
INTERACTIVITY

Explore feeding adaptations of animals in a coral reef ecosystem.

Surprise at the Birdfeeder!
Figure 1 In Brevard, North Carolina, about one-third of the Eastern gray squirrel population is white. In 1949, a resident received a pair of white squirrels as a gift. When one squirrel escaped, the other was released to join its friend. Soon after, people began to spot more white squirrels in town.

Organizing Life

Figure 2 Linnaeus classified life based on the structures of each organism.

Classify ✎ Identify three characteristics that you can observe in the image and list them below. Assign each characteristic a shape: a circle, rectangle, or triangle. Using the characteristics you have identified, organize the organisms in the image into three groups by drawing the appropriate shapes around them.

....

....

....

....

....

....

....

📖 **Make Meaning** What problem or question have you had that required you to make observations and gather evidence to figure it out?

Linnaeus' System of Classification

Carolus Linnaeus (1707–1778) developed the first scientific system for classifying and naming living things. Linnaeus collected samples of organisms from around the world. When classifying the organisms according to shared characteristics like those shown in **Figure 2**, he observed that there were variations of traits within a species. He was able to describe the variations and diversity of life, but not explain what caused that variation and diversity. No one was yet exploring how organisms came to be the way they are. In fact, many people still believed that organisms could appear out of the air as if by magic.

Lamarck's Idea

The first serious attempts to explain evolution began in the late 1700s. A French scientist, Jean-Baptiste Lamarck (1744–1829), was put in charge of a museum department of "Insects and Worms," which also included all the invertebrates, or animals without backbones. Lamarck devoted himself to learning everything he could about invertebrates. Unlike Linnaeus, Lamarck wasn't satisfied with describing what the animals looked like. Instead, Lamarck attempted to figure out how the organisms came to be. After much study, Lamarck developed the first attempt at a scientific hypothesis explaining how species change over time.

Lamarck's Hypothesis of Transformation Lamarck mistakenly believed that organisms could change their traits by selectively using or not using various parts of their bodies. For example, moles could develop long, strong claws by digging through dirt. Lamarck **hypothesized** that if two adult moles with long claws mated, their offspring would inherit those claws, as shown in **Figure 3**. In the next generation, the individuals who used their claws more would pass even longer claws on to their offspring. In this way, the whole population of moles would gradually grow bigger, stronger claws, until they reached the form we see today.

Lamarck's transformation hypothesis doesn't support a consistent pattern for other traits when investigated further. It doesn't explain how features such as eyes could have developed. The hypothesis also does not work when tested with experiments. For example, you can force a plant to grow sideways. However, the offspring of the plant grow straight up toward the light. While his hypothesis was not supported, Lamarck did contribute some important new ideas. First, he suggested that a change in a species takes place by small, gradual steps. Second, he proposed that simple organisms could develop over many generations into more complex organisms.

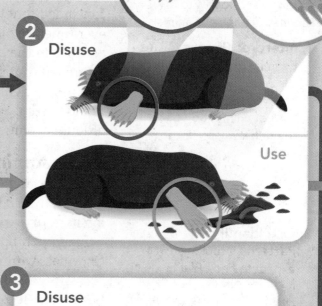

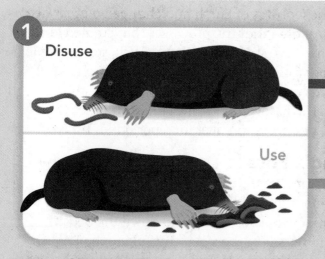

Lamarck's Transformation Hypothesis
Figure 3 🖊 In the open space, draw what you think the offspring of the mole that did not dig for food will look like, based on Lamarck's hypothesis.

☑ CHECK POINT **Determine Conclusions** Why was Lamarck's hypothesis not accepted?

....

....

....

Reading the Past

Figure 4 Charles Lyell discovered how to read Earth's history from layers of rock. Meanwhile, Mary Anning used fossils to reconstruct ancient animals.

1. Interpret Photos
   Examine the fossil. List the parts of the animal that you recognize. What kind of animal do you think this was?

   ....

   ....

   ....

2. CCC Identify
   Patterns Would you expect to find older or newer fossils in rock layers closer to the surface? Why?

   ....

   ....

   ....

   ....

   ....

Charles Lyell's Rocks

Not long after Lamarck proposed his ideas, a young lawyer named Charles Lyell (1797–1875) began studying naturally-formed layers of rocks and fossils, like those in **Figure 4**. A **fossil** is the preserved remains or traces of an organism that lived in the past. Lyell concluded that the features of Earth had changed a great deal over time. He also stated that the processes that created land features in the past were still active. Before Lyell, some people estimated that the world was less than 6,000 years old. Lyell and other scientists pushed that estimate back more than 300 million years. Lyell's discoveries set the stage for a theory of gradual evolution, or evolution over long periods of time.

Mary Anning's Fossils

Mary Anning (1799–1847) lived a much different life than Linnaeus, Lamarck, or Lyell. Coming from a poor family that made money by collecting fossils, Mary Anning would roam up and down the beach while searching for fossils in the steep cliffs along the English Channel. Anning taught herself how to reconstruct the bodies of fossilized animals. Many of these animals had never before been seen. Because of Anning's work, scientists began to realize that some animals had lived in the ancient past but no longer existed. While Anning had no formal training as a scientist, her observations and discoveries made her a key contributor in the study of both fossils and geology.

✓ CHECK POINT **Summarize Text** How did the scientists show that organisms and Earth changed over time?

....

....

Darwin's Journey

In 1831, 22-year-old Charles Darwin set out on a five-year trip around the world aboard a British navy ship, the HMS *Beagle*. Darwin was a naturalist—a person who observes and studies the natural world. The captain of the *Beagle* wanted someone aboard who could make and record observations as the crew explored South America. One of Darwin's professors suggested inviting Darwin. And thus was launched a brilliant career!

Darwin was surprised to see the diversity of living things he encountered during the voyage. He saw insects that looked like flowers. He also saw armadillos digging insects from the ground. These mammals with a leathery shell that looks like a small suit of armor would have been very strange creatures to see. Today, scientists know that organisms are even more diverse than Darwin thought. Scientists have calculated that there are millions of species on Earth—and new ones are being identified all the time. Scientists have no way to estimate how many undiscovered species exist, but they believe the numbers are very high.

Fossils

On his journey aboard the *Beagle*, Darwin also saw fossils of animals that had died long ago. Some of the fossils he observed confused him. **Figure 5** shows fossils Darwin found that resembled the bones of living armadillos but were much larger in size. Darwin wondered what had happened to the ancient, giant armadillos. Over long periods of time, could the giant armadillos have evolved into the smaller species we see today?

Armored Animals

Figure 5 Darwin thought that the fossil bones of giant Glyptodons (right) resembled the bones of modern armadillos (left).

1. **Determine Similarities** List two common features that the animals share.

....

....

2. **Infer** Why might these features be important to both ancient and modern armadillos?

....

....

....

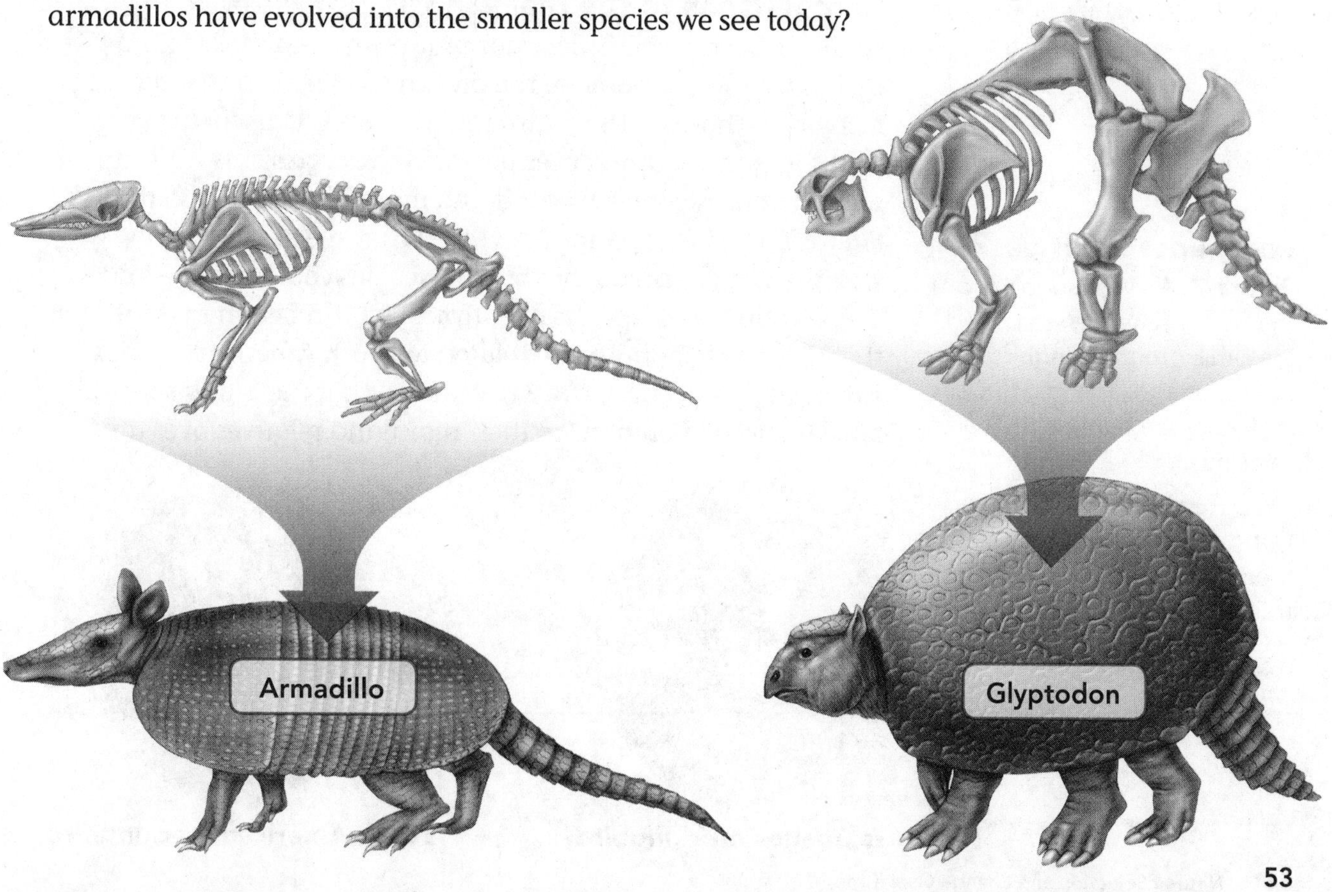

Armadillo

Glyptodon

53

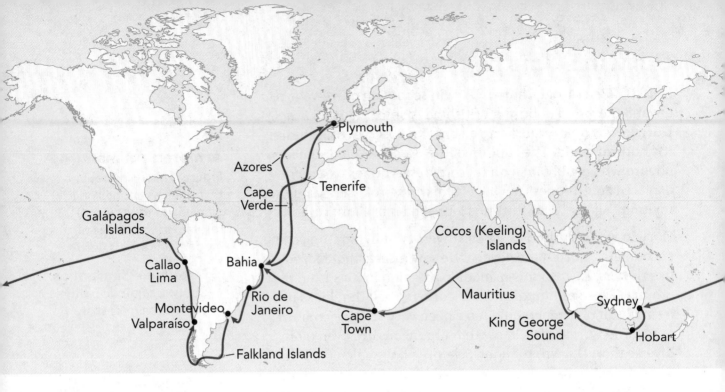

Voyage of the HMS Beagle, 1831–1836

Figure 6 Darwin sailed 40,000 miles around the world during his five-year voyage.

👆 **INTERACTIVITY**

Observe organisms that Darwin encountered in the Galápagos Islands.

Long-Lost Relatives?

Figure 7 🖊 Mockingbirds on the South American mainland are similar to mockingbirds on the Galápagos Islands. Circle and label the features that are not similar.

CCC Relate Structure and Function Why do you think these birds have different traits?

....

....

....

....

Galápagos Organisms

The *Beagle* sailed to many different locations, as shown in **Figure 6**, and made several stops along the coast of South America. From what is now Peru on the Pacific coast, the ship traveled west to the Galápagos Islands. Darwin observed many different life forms there. He compared organisms from the Galápagos Islands to organisms that lived elsewhere. He also compared organisms living on the different islands.

Comparisons to the Mainland

Darwin discovered similarities between Galápagos organisms and those found in South America. Some of the birds and plants on the islands resembled those on the mainland. However, Darwin also noted important differences between the organisms. You can see differences between island and mainland mockingbirds in **Figure 7**. Darwin became convinced that species do not always stay the same. Instead, he thought species could change and even produce new species over time. Darwin began to think that the island species might be related to South American species. After much reflection, Darwin realized that the island species had become different from their mainland relatives over time.

Galápagos mockingbird

South American mockingbird

Comparisons Among the Islands Darwin collected birds from several of the Galápagos Islands. The birds were a little different from one island to the next. Darwin would learn that the birds were all types of finches. He concluded that the finch species were all related to a single common ancestor species that came from the mainland. Over time, different finches developed different beak shapes and sizes that were well suited to the food they ate. Beak shape is an example of an **adaptation**—an inherited behavior or physical characteristic that helps an organism survive and reproduce in its environment. Look at **Figure 8**. Birds with narrow, prying beaks can grasp insects. Those with long, pointed, sharp beaks can pick at cacti. Short, hooked beaks tear open fruit, while short, wide beaks crush seeds.

☑ CHECK POINT **Determine Central Ideas** What convinced Darwin that species can change over time?

....

....

Question It!

We Got the Beak!

SEP Construct Explanations The finches in **Figure 8** show variations due to adaptation. Suppose someone asks what could cause a species' beak to change. How would you answer the person?

....

....

....

....

....

Galápagos Finches
Figure 8 Darwin observed beak adaptations.

1. Claim Why is it necessary for finches to have different beaks?

....

....

....

....

....

2. Evidence ✎ Draw an arrow from each finch matching it to the type of food you think it eats.

3. Reasoning Explain why your evidence supports your claim.

....

....

....

....

....

....

....

Darwin's Hypothesis Darwin thought about what he had observed during his voyage on the *Beagle*. By this time, while Darwin was convinced that organisms change over time, he wanted to know how the organisms changed. Darwin consulted other scientists and gathered more information. Based on his observations, Darwin reasoned that plants or animals that arrived on the Galápagos Islands faced conditions different from those on the nearby mainland. Darwin hypothesized that species change over many generations and become better adapted to new conditions. Darwin's hypothesis was an idea that contributed important new knowledge. Later, he and other scientists used it to test and develop a scientific theory.

Developing a Theory In science, a theory explains why and how things happen in nature. A **scientific theory** is a well-tested explanation for a wide range of observations and experimental results. Based on a body of facts, scientific theory is confirmed repeatedly through observation and experimentation. Darwin's ideas are often referred to as the theory of evolution. From the evidence he collected, and from all the discoveries of the scientists who had come before him, Darwin concluded that organisms on the Galápagos Islands had changed over time, or evolved.

☑ **CHECK POINT** **Cite Textual Evidence** Why do you think theories, like Darwin's theory of evolution, are important to science?

....

....

....

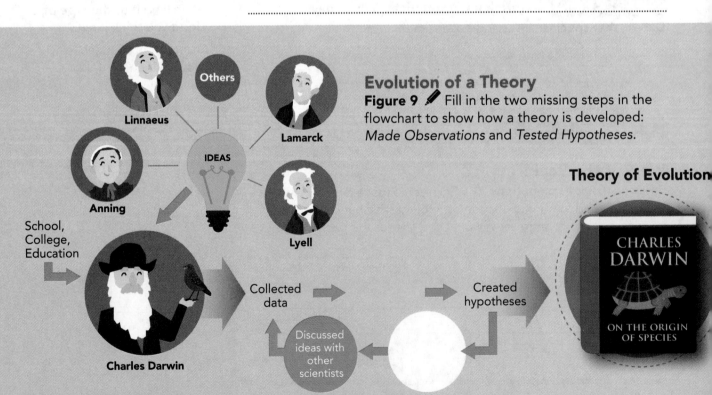

Evolution of a Theory
Figure 9 ✏ Fill in the two missing steps in the flowchart to show how a theory is developed: *Made Observations* and *Tested Hypotheses.*

Theory of Evolution

Others

Linnaeus

Lamarck

IDEAS

Anning

Lyell

School, College, Education

Charles Darwin

Collected data

Discussed ideas with other scientists

Created hypotheses

CHARLES DARWIN

ON THE ORIGIN OF SPECIES

MS-LS4-4

1. **Identify** Name four people, other than Darwin, whose work contributed to the study of evolution.

....

2. **Apply Scientific Reasoning** Why are fossils important to developing a theory of evolution?

....
....
....
....

3. **Compare and Contrast** How are variations and adaptations similar? How are they different?

....
....
....
....
....
....

4. **Integrate Information** Which two ideas of Lamarck contributed the most to Darwin's theory of evolution?

....
....
....
....
....

5. **SEP Construct Explanations** If the finches on the Galápagos Islands had such different beaks, how could Darwin think they shared a common ancestor from the mainland?

....
....
....
....
....
....
....

Quest CHECK-IN

In this lesson, you learned about adaptations and variations as well as the people whose ideas and activities contributed to understanding how organisms change over time. You also learned how Darwin developed his theory of evolution.

CCC Stability and Change Consider what you learned about variation and how species change over time. Why is it important to understand how a different migration route might be affecting the blackcaps' physical traits?

....
....
....
....

☞ INTERACTIVITY

Meet the Blackcaps

Go online to draw conclusions about the variations between the two groups, based on what you've learned about where the birds migrate in winter.

HANDS-ON LAB

u**Investigate** Measure variation
in plant and animal populations.

MS-LS4-4 Construct an explanation based on evidence
that describes how genetic variations of traits in a
population increase some individuals' probability of
surviving and reproducing in a specific environment.

MS-LS4-5 Gather and synthesize information about the
technologies that have changed the way humans influence
the inheritance of desired traits in organisms.

MS-LS4-6 Use mathematical representations to support
explanations of how natural selection may lead to increases
and decreases of specific traits in populations over time.

Connect It!

✏ **Estimate how many dead fish are shown here. Write your estimation on
the photograph.**

Explain Phenomena Some fish survived this event, known as a fish kill. What
might be different about the fish that survived?

....

....

Apply Scientific Reasoning If low oxygen levels occur every year and cause fish
kills, how might the population of fish change over time?

....

Evolution by Natural Selection

Living in a small body of water can be dangerous for fish. If water conditions become unhealthy, there is nowhere for the fish to go. Too little rain, too many fish, and an overgrowth of algae can work together to reduce oxygen levels in water. **Figure 1** shows what happened when oxygen levels fell too low. A "fish kill" can wipe out most of the local population of a species of fish. Some individuals, however, usually survive the disaster. These fish will live to reproduce, thus ensuring the species survives.

Darwin's Search for a Mechanism

After his return to England, Darwin was not satisfied with his theory of evolution. He struggled to determine evolution's mechanism. A **mechanism** is the natural process by which something takes place. Darwin asked himself how organisms could change over time. And how could a species become better adapted to new conditions? To solve this mystery, Darwin performed experiments and read the works of other naturalists and scientists.

INTERACTIVITY

Investigate how a species of butterflyfish adapts to changes in its environment.

Fish Kill

Figure 1 Fish can survive only in water with dissolved oxygen. When oxygen levels fall too low, thousands of fish can perish at once.

Rock pigeon
(*Columba livia*)

Fantail pigeon

Silky fantail pigeon

Fancy Pigeons

Figure 2 Through artificial selection, Darwin helped to create the fantail pigeon (center) from the wild rock pigeon (left). Silky fantails (right) were then bred from the fantail pigeon. Despite their physical differences, these two breeds belong to the same species as the rock pigeon, *Columba livia*.

Make Observations List the differences you see between the three different pigeon types.

📓 **Write About It**
Farmers often selectively breed farm animals. When farmers breed and care for farm animals with certain genetic traits that humans desire, it is called animal husbandry. Write about how animal husbandry affects society. Consider farmers, restaurants, grocery stores, consumers, and the use of land resources.

Literacy Connection

Cite Textual Evidence As you read about natural selection, underline sentences or parts of sentences that you can refer to later to help you support your explanations about this process.

Artificial Selection Darwin studied farm and pet animals produced by artificial selection. In artificial selection, humans have the capacity to influence certain characteristics of organisms by breeding them selectively. Organisms with a desired parental trait, such as color, are bred by humans who calculate the probability of offspring inheriting the trait. Darwin himself bred pigeons with large, fan-shaped tails (**Figure 2**). He repeatedly allowed only those pigeons with many tail feathers to mate. In this way, Darwin produced pigeons with two or three times the usual number of tail feathers. Darwin thought that a process similar to artificial selection might happen in nature. But he wondered what natural process resulted in the selection.

Natural Selection Darwin understood how evolution could work when he read an essay by Thomas Malthus. Malthus noted that both animals and humans can produce many offspring. If all the offspring survived, the world would quickly become overpopulated. There would not be enough food for everyone, and part of the population would starve. Darwin realized that some individuals have traits that help them to survive and reproduce. If these traits are hereditary, they can be passed on to the next generation. Gradually, over many generations, more and more individuals will have the helpful traits.

The Origin of Species Darwin waited a long time to publish his ideas. He thought they might be too revolutionary for the public to accept. Then, in 1858, Alfred Russel Wallace sent Darwin a letter. Wallace had also read Malthus' work and discovered the same mechanism for evolution! The next year, Darwin published his theory in *The Origin of Species*. In his book, Darwin proposed that evolution occurs by means of **natural selection**, a process by which individuals that are better adapted to their environment are more likely to survive and reproduce than other members of the same species.

How Natural Selection Works
Darwin identified three factors that affect the process of natural selection: overproduction, variation, and competition. First, there must be overproduction, shown in **Figure 3** below. Darwin knew that most species produce more offspring than can possibly survive. Secondly, there must be variation. Members of a population differ from one another in many of their traits. For example, sea turtles may differ in color, size, the ability to crawl quickly on sand, and shell hardness. Such variations are hereditary, passed from parents to offspring through genetic material. Finally, there must be **competition**—the struggle among living things to get the necessary amount of food, water, and shelter. In many species, so many offspring are produced that there are not enough resources—food, water, and living space—for all of them.

✅ CHECK POINT **Summarize** What are the factors that affect the process of natural selection?

....

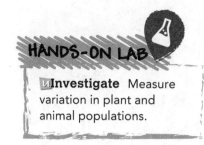

HANDS-ON LAB

🔬Investigate Measure variation in plant and animal populations.

Overproduction
Figure 3 Brown rats can give birth up to 12 times each year with about 6 to 11 pups in each litter. The young rats are ready to breed when they are 12 weeks old.

1. **SEP Analyze Data** About how many pups can each female rat produce every year?

....

2. **Draw Conclusions** Why can't every rat survive and reproduce at its maximum rate?

....
....
....
....
....
....
....

Adaptations and Selection

Figure 4 Once sea turtles hatch from a nest, they must be fast and strong enough to reach the ocean before predators arrive.

Selection Darwin observed that some traits make individuals better adapted to their environment. Those individuals were more likely to survive and reproduce, and their offspring would inherit the helpful trait. The offspring, in turn, would be more likely to survive and reproduce and pass the trait to their offspring. After many generations, the proportion of this helpful trait increases in the population. This is called *predominance* of that trait. The proportion of less helpful traits tends to decrease, a process called *suppression*. **Figure 4** illustrates how conditions in the environment select sea turtles with helpful traits to become parents of the next generation. Darwin proposed that, over a long time, natural selection can lead to change.

☑ **CHECK POINT** **Cite Textual Evidence** How is Darwin's proposal that natural selection can lead to change in a species supported in nature?

....

....

....

Math Toolbox

Hatching for Success

Sea turtles play an important role in maintaining Florida's coastal ecosystem.

1. **Graph Proportional Relationships** ✏ Complete the graph to compare the total number of sea turtle nests at each beach to the number of nests that hatched sea turtles. Create a key next to the graph.

2. **SEP Construct an Explanation** On which beach(es) would you create a turtle refuge? Cite evidence to support your response.

....

....

....

Beach	Total Nests	Hatched Nests
Barefoot Beach	174	50
City of Naples	148	14
Delnor Wiggins	46	6
Marco Island	52	15
10,000 Islands	87	13

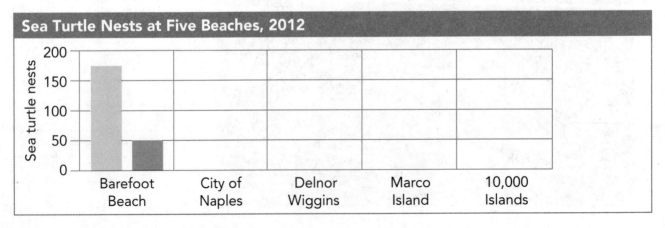

Sea Turtle Nests at Five Beaches, 2012

Environmental Change A change in the environment can affect an organism's ability to survive and may therefore lead to natural selection. For example, a storm can topple many trees in a forest. Trees that are better able to withstand strong winds have a survival advantage. In **Figure 5** you can see how natural selection might result in a shift in the population toward storm-resistant trees.

Natural Selection in Action

Figure 5 Natural events can lead to selection for favorable traits in a population. Read each image caption and use evidence to answer each question.

1990: Biologists survey a forest.

SEP Use Models List your observations related to the variation, competition, and overproduction of this tree population.

....

....

....

1991: Same forest after a windstorm.

Explain Phenomena What helpful trait did most of the surviving trees have?

....

....

....

2010: Same forest is surveyed again.

Make Observations How is the population different now compared to 1990?

....

....

2017: Another windstorm hits.

SEP Develop Models ✐ In the space provided, draw the effect of the storm on the forest.

SEP Construct Explanations How will natural selection have changed the forest from 1990 to 2030?

....

....

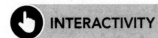

INTERACTIVITY

Analyze data on how a
mouse population changes.

VIRTUAL LAB

Investigate how natural
selection affects population
traits over time.

Genes and Natural Selection Darwin did a
brilliant job of explaining natural selection, but he was never
able to figure out where variations come from. He also did not
understand how traits were passed from parents to offspring.
Darwin hypothesized that tiny particles from around the
parents' bodies passed into the developing offspring. Even at
the time, Darwin realized that this explanation was flawed.
Yet he did not have enough information to formulate a better
explanation. Recall Gregor Mendel and his study of heredity
and genetics. Mendel's experiments in plant breeding took
place during Darwin's life. His work showed that parents pass
genes to their offspring. Genes are units of genetic material that
provide instructions for a specific protein or function. Inherited
variations result from individuals having different combinations of genes, as shown in **Figure 6**. Your hair color, eye color—
and dimples, if you have them—are all determined by the genes
your parents passed to you. Only traits controlled by genes can
be acted upon by natural selection. Genetic variations contribute to the diversity of organisms.

Inherited Traits

Figure 6 Variations in traits depend on the traits that parents pass on to
their offspring.

1. Make Observations List several inherited variations you can observe
in this group of students.

....

....

....

....

....

....

....

....

....

....

....

2. CCC Cause and Effect How did the students in **Figure 6** get such
variations in traits?

....

....

Figure 7 A mutation caused the flower on the right to grow in an unusual way.

Explain Phenomena Describe how the mutation changed the flower.

....

....

....

....

Mutations Sexual reproduction causes existing gene variations to be recombined in each member of a population. To get a new variation, there must be a gene mutation. A mutation is any change to the genetic material. **Figure 7** shows a flower with an obvious mutation. Only mutations to sex chromosomes can be passed on to offspring. In humans, new genetic variations are introduced by mutations to egg or sperm cells. A mutation to a body cell, such as a heart or brain cell, only affects the individual and is not passed on to offspring. If offspring are born with a mutation, natural selection will determine whether that mutation gets passed on to the next generation.

 INTERACTIVITY

Explore how a lack of genetic variations can impact crops.

 VIDEO

Watch a video about natural selection.

Epigenetic Changes Epigenetics is the study of small changes to DNA that turn genes on or off but do not change the genetic code itself. All the cells in your body have identical DNA, but functions vary greatly. Gene expression determines how a cell acts—whether it will function as a bone cell or a skin cell. In your lifetime, there will be small chemical changes to your DNA affecting how genes get expressed. Your offspring can inherit these changes.

Inherited changes can affect multiple generations. For example, smoking makes small changes to DNA. Due to epigenetics, a grandmother who smokes is more likely to have a grandchild with asthma. The grandchild will inherit the same epigenetic changes that smoking caused in his or her grandmother. Epigenetics is challenging the idea that natural selection acts on genetic variation alone. Scientists are working to understand how a gene that gets turned on or off in a body cell could show up two generations later.

✓ CHECK POINT **Distinguish Facts** A mutation can be inherited only if it occurs in which type of cell?

....

☑ LESSON 2 Check

MS-LS4-4, MS-LS4-5, MS-LS4-6

1. **Identify** Darwin identified three factors affecting the process of natural selection. What are they?

....

2. **Determine Differences** The terms *mechanism* and *natural selection* both refer to natural processes. What makes them different?

....

....

....

....

3. **Evaluate Claims** A classmate claims that all mutations are harmful and can be passed on. Is this true? Explain.

....

....

....

....

....

4. **Apply Scientific Reasoning** How does natural selection help a species to evolve?

....

....

....

5. **SEP Construct Explanations** How does the genetic variation of traits within a population affect its probability for survival? Explain.

....

....

....

....

....

....

6. **CCC Cause and Effect** Sea turtles can lay 50 to 200 eggs in a nest. Some eggs get destroyed or eaten by other animals. The young turtles that hatch face many challenges as they head to the ocean. They may have to crawl over steep slopes, through seaweed, or around obstacles. Raccoons, foxes, crabs, birds, fish, and sharks may eat them. Given the challenges and the data in the Math Toolbox, write an expression and use it to calculate the percent hatched. Use the percent to roughly estimate the number of sea turtles from a nest of 100 in Naples that reach the ocean safely. Express your answer as a percentage.

....

....

....

....

....

....

7. **SEP Develop Models** 🖊 Draw a young turtle and the variations you think could make it more successful. Label the variations and explain how they would benefit the turtle.

Fossils from Bedrock

▶ VIDEO

Explore the techniques and technologies that scientists use to extract fossils.

Do you know how to get a fossil out of a rock? You engineer it! Scientists use several methods to extract these remains of the past.

The Challenge: To remove fossils from bedrock without damaging them or the surrounding area.

Phenomenon Fossils stay trapped under layers of rock for millions of years. When the geology of an area changes, these layers are sometimes exposed. This offers a great opportunity to search for evidence of how adaptation by natural selection contributes to the evolution of a species.

Scientists carefully brush away dirt and debris from bones discovered in dig sites to gather fossil evidence of how organisms have changed over time.

Removing a fragile fossil from rock takes skill, time, and special tools. Sometimes fossil collectors have to dig out the larger section of rock holding a fossil. Until recently, extracting a fossil meant slowly and carefully chipping away at the rock with a small chisel and hammer, then sweeping away rock dust with a small brush. The latest technology is the pneumatic drill pen. Vibrating at 30,000 times each minute, the drill pen carves out a fossil more quickly and with greater control. Another method is the acid wash. While it takes much longer than the mechanical methods, and can only be used on fossils found in limestone and chalk, an acid wash is the safest way to remove an undamaged fossil.

DESIGN CHALLENGE

How would you modify the process for removing fossils from bedrock? Go to the Engineering Design Notebook to find out!

HANDS-ON LAB

µInvestigate Explore how different birds' feet help them survive in their environments.

MS-LS3-1 Develop and use a model to describe why structural changes to genes (mutations) located on chromosomes may affect proteins and may result in harmful, beneficial, or neutral effects to the structure and function of the organism.

MS-LS4-4 Construct an explanation based on evidence that describes how genetic variations of traits in a population increase some individuals' probability of surviving and reproducing in a specific environment.

MS-LS4-6 Use mathematical representations to support explanations of how natural selection may lead to increases and decreases of specific traits in populations over time.

Connect It!

✏ **Label each duck as either male or female.**

SEP Construct Explanations Do you think that both ducks' appearance could be a result of natural selection? Explain your reasoning.

....

....

....

Processes of Evolution

Charles Darwin's theory of natural selection is straightforward. Any population of living things has inherited variations. In addition, the population produces more young than can survive. According to natural selection, only the individuals that are well-adapted to their environments will survive and reproduce. An organism's **fitness** describes how well it can survive and reproduce in its environment. According to Darwin's theory, the fittest individuals survive to reproduce and pass their traits to the next generation. Organisms with low fitness are not as well-adapted to their environment and may die without reproducing or may not have as many offspring. Over time, as individual organisms successfully respond to changing conditions in the environment, the population evolves and its fitness increases.

Beyond Natural Selection Observe the male and female mandarin ducks in **Figure 1**. Both ducks have many adaptations that help them survive and reproduce in their watery habitat. Oily feathers keep the ducks dry. Webbed feet propel the ducks quickly through the water. Nesting in trees keeps ducklings safe from predators. Dull colors help the female duck blend in with her background. Now, look at the male duck. He seems to be calling for attention! His brightly colored face and the bold black and white stripes on his sides surely attract predators. How could natural selection result in traits that hurt the male duck's chance of survival? Answer: There is more to evolution than "survival of the fittest."

HANDS-ON LAB

Investigate Explore how different birds' feet help them survive in their environments.

▶ VIDEO

Learn about the process of evolution.

Opposites Attract

Figure 1 Believe it or not, these ducks are both from the same species. Male and female mandarin ducks have evolved to look very different!

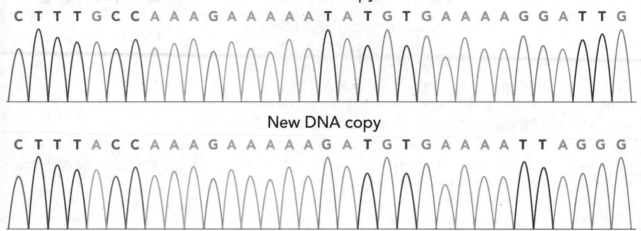

Old DNA copy

C T T T G C C A A A G A A A A A T A T G T G A A A A G G A T T G

New DNA copy

C T T T A C C A A A G A A A A A A G A T G T G A A A A T T A G G G

Spellcheck, Please!

Figure 2 🖊 A mutation is like a spelling error in a gene's DNA sequence. Any change in the sequence results in a mutation. Observe how the sequence changes. Compare the sequences of the two DNA copies. Circle any differences you observe in the new DNA copy.

Explain Phenomena What do you think may have caused the differences between the two DNA copies?

....

....

Literacy Connection

Determine Conclusions
Why is it that mutations to body cells do not affect offspring?

....

....

....

....

....

....

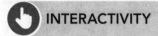

INTERACTIVITY

Analyze mutations and how they can impact evolution.

Mutations One reason for Darwin's oversimplification of evolution was that he did not yet know about mutations. You've already learned that a mutation is any change to an organism's genetic material. Mutations can create multiple alleles, or forms of a gene. Different alleles cause variations in traits such as eye color, ear shape, and blood type.

How Mutations Happen Mutations are created in two ways. First, a dividing cell can make an error while copying its DNA (**Figure 2**). There are approximately six billion units in one copy of human DNA. Imagine copying by hand a book that had six billion letters. Think how easy it would be to make a mistake! Researchers estimate that each human child inherits an average of 60 new mutations from his or her parents. That sounds like a lot, doesn't it? But it means that the body makes only one mistake out of every 100 million units of DNA copied. Secondly, mutations also occur when an organism is exposed to environmental factors such as radiation or certain chemicals that damage the cell's DNA. While the cell has mechanisms to repair damaged DNA, that repair is not always perfect. Any mistake while fixing the DNA results in a mutation.

Effects of Mutations Most mutations are neutral—they have no effect on the individual's function. The mutation may be in a part of the DNA that is inactive. Out of the mutations that do affect function, most are harmful to the individual. **Randomly** changing a process in the body typically results in decreased function. Only mutations on sex chromosomes can get passed on and affect the fitness of offspring. A beneficial mutation that increases fitness tends to grow more common in a population. A mutation that decreases fitness tends to disappear because the individuals with that mutation die or reproduce less successfully.

Need for Mutations People often think of mutations as harmful. It's true that mutations can lead to cancer and genetic defects. At the same time, however, mutations are necessary for evolution to occur. Mutations create all the variations among members of a species and account for the diversity of organisms on Earth. **Figure 3** shows how mutations can change plant leaf shapes. Imagine if the first single-celled organisms had never experienced mutation! That first species would have been the only life that ever existed on the planet.

☑ CHECK POINT **Summarize Text** How are mutations both harmful and beneficial?

....

....

Academic Vocabulary
List where you may have heard the word *random* used before. What does *randomly* mean as it's used here?

....

....

....

....

....

👆 **INTERACTIVITY**

Explore what might happen when a population of squirrels is separated by landforms.

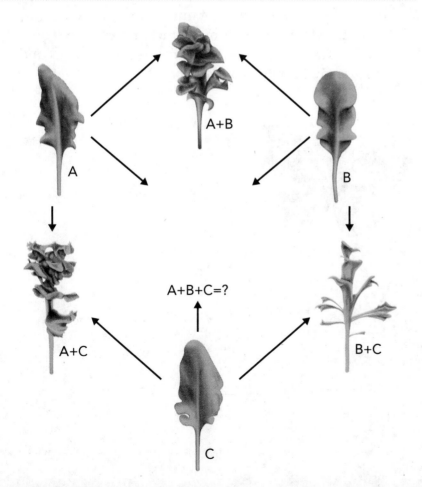

Variations from Mutations
Figure 3 Scientists studied how three mutations in mustard plant DNA (labeled A, B, and C in the image) affect leaf shape.

SEP Use a Model to Predict 🖊 Examine the effects of the mutations on leaf shape. In the center of the image, draw what you think the leaves would look like if a plant had all three mutations.

Coevolution and Cooperation

Figure 4 The acacia tree and ants both evolved features that help them work together.

Infer What features do you think the acacia tree and the ants might have that would help one another?

....

....

....

....

....

Coevolution

Two or more species with close **interactions** can affect each other's evolution. Coevolution is the process by which two species evolve in response to changes in each other over time. Coevolution can happen when species cooperate with each other, as shown in **Figure 4**. Several acacia trees in Central America have coevolved with select species of ants. The acacia trees evolved hollow thorns and nectar pores because of their close interactions with the ants. Likewise, the ants evolved defense behaviors to protect "their" trees. A queen ant lays her eggs in the hollow thorns of an acacia tree. In return for the shelter and food from the tree, the ants protect the tree. They attack when other insects or animals try to devour the acacia leaves. Other examples of interactions that can lead to coevolution include species that compete for resources and species that may be prey to a predator.

Mimicry in Coevolution

Figure 5 Tiger-wing butterflies evolved to absorb and store toxins from plants they ate when they were caterpillars. This makes them taste bad. Birds avoid eating tiger-wing butterflies and other butterflies that mimic, or closely resemble, them.

SEP Develop Models ✎ Sketch the progression of how a butterfly's wing patterns may have changed over time to mimic that of the tiger-wing butterfly.

☑ LESSON 3 Check

MS-LS3-1, MS-LS4-4, MS-LS4-6

1. **SEP Communicate Information** What does fitness mean in terms of evolution?

....
....
....
....

2. **Apply Scientific Reasoning** What are the two ways in which mutations can occur? Give at least one example of an environmental factor.

....
....
....
....
....

3. **SEP Construct Explanations** Explain the role of mutations in genetic variation and in the diversity of living things. Support your explanation with evidence.

....
....
....
....
....
....
....
....
....

4. **Distinguish Relationships** Consider two species that compete for the same resources. Could their interactions affect each other's evolution? Explain.

....
....
....
....
....
....

Quest CHECK-IN

In this lesson, you learned how a population can be influenced by natural selection, species interactions, and genetic variations due to mutations.

CCC Cause and Effect Why is it important to consider the role of genetic variations when trying to determine what caused the changes to the European blackcaps?

....
....
....
....

INTERACTIVITY

Evolution of the Blackcaps

Go online to investigate factors that may have caused the variations in the European blackcaps.

LESSON 4

Evidence in the Fossil Record

HANDS-ON LAB

µInvestigate Model how different fossils form.

MS-LS4-1 Analyze and interpret data for patterns in the fossil record that document the existence, diversity, extinction, and change of life forms throughout the history of life on Earth under the assumption that natural laws operate today as in the past.

MS-LS4-2 Apply scientific ideas to construct an explanation for the anatomical similarities and differences among modern organisms and between modern and fossil organisms to infer evolutionary relationships.

MS-LS4-3 Analyze displays of pictorial data to compare patterns of similarities in the embryological development across multiple species to identify relationships not evident in the fully formed anatomy.

MS-LS4-6 Use mathematical representations to support explanations of how natural selection may lead to increases and decreases of specific traits in populations over time. (Also **EP&CIIa and EP&CIIc**)

Connect It !

✏ **Draw arrows to connect similar features between the fossil and the modern animal.**

Interpret Photos Which parts of the crinoid's tentacles are best preserved in the fossils? Which parts were not preserved?

....

....

....

The Fossil Record

Fossils are preserved remains or traces of living things. **Figure 1** shows fossils of crinoids, relatives of modern-day starfish. All the fossils that have been discovered and what we have learned from them make up the **fossil record**. It is called a record because the fossils form data patterns that scientists can understand through measurement and observation. The fossil record documents the diversity of the life forms, many now extinct, and shows how life forms existed and changed throughout Earth's history. The fossil record is a treasure trove of **evidence** about how organisms of the past evolved into the forms we see today.

Microevolution and Macroevolution

Scientists can observe evolution taking place within populations of organisms. Small, gradual changes in the color or size of a certain population is called microevolution. *Micro-* means very small, and *evolution* means change through time. One example of microevolution is the northern population of house sparrows. They adapted to a colder climate by growing larger bodies than the southern population. This small change took less than 100 years. Usually, for multicellular organisms, it takes years to thousands of years for a new species to develop. Scientists turn to the fossil record to learn about macroevolution, or major evolutionary change.

Academic Vocabulary

Where have you read or heard the word *evidence* used before? List at least one synonym for *evidence*.

....

....

....

....

A Glimpse of the Past

Figure 1 Crinoids are relatives of starfish. We can learn a lot about the evolution of crinoids by looking at fossils of their extinct relatives. Some ancient crinoids grew more than 40 meters long!

1. **An organism dies and sinks to the bottom of a lake.**

2.

Forming a Fossil

Figure 2 A fossil may form when sediment quickly covers a dead organism.

Relate Text to Visuals
🖉 The images and captions are shown in the correct order. Fill in the missing caption for image 2.

How Fossils Form

A fossil is the impression that an organism or part of an organism leaves in rock. That impression comes about in one of two ways. A mold creates a hollow area in the rock that is the shape of an organism or part of an organism. Or, a cast makes a solid copy of an organism's shape, sometimes containing some of the original organism.

Most fossils form when living things die and sediment buries them. Sediment is the small, solid pieces of material that come from rocks or the remains of organisms and settle to the bottom of a body of water. Over time, the sediment slowly hardens into rock and preserves the shapes of the organisms. Fossils can form from any kind of living thing, from bacteria to dinosaurs.

Many fossils come from organisms that once lived in or near still water. Swamps, lakes, and shallow seas build up sediment quickly and bury remains of living things. In **Figure 2**, you can see how a fossil might form. When an organism dies, its soft parts usually decay quickly or are eaten by other organisms. Only hard parts of an organism typically leave fossils. These hard parts include bones, shells, teeth, seeds, and woody stems. It is rare for the soft parts of an organism to become a fossil. People often see fossils after erosion exposes them. Erosion is the wearing away of Earth's surface by natural processes such as water and wind.

Many Kinds of Fossils

Figure 3 A fossil may be the preserved remains of an organism's body, or the trace of an organism—something it leaves behind.

1. **Classify** 🖉 Label each image as either a body fossil or a trace fossil.

2. **SEP Evaluate Evidence** Why did you classify them that way?

....
....
....
....
....
....

Snail shells

Turtle dropping

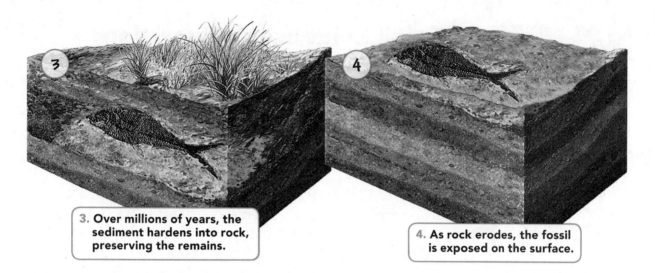

3. **Over millions of years, the sediment hardens into rock, preserving the remains.**

4. **As rock erodes, the fossil is exposed on the surface.**

Kinds of Fossils There are two types of fossils: body fossils and trace fossils. Each one gives us different information about the ancient organism it represents.

Body Fossils Body fossils preserve the shape and structure of an organism. We can learn about what a plant or animal looked like from a body fossil. Body fossils of trees are called petrified wood. The term *petrified* means "turned into stone." Petrified fossils are fossils in which minerals replace all or part of an organism. In petrified wood, the remains are so well preserved that scientists can often count the rings to tell how old a tree was when it died millions of years ago. Ancient mammoths frozen into ice, petrified dinosaur bones, and insects trapped in amber are other examples of body fossils.

Trace Fossils We can learn what an animal did from trace fossils. Footprints, nests, and animal droppings preserved in stone are all trace fossils, as shown in **Figure 3**.

HANDS-ON LAB

Investigate Model how different fossils form.

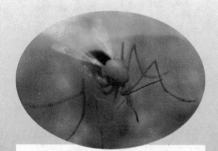

Mosquito in amber

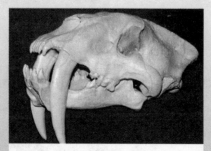

Smilodon, cat skull

Dinosaur tracks

Literacy Connection

Summarize Text At the end of each two-page spread, stop and summarize what you just read to a classmate.

Fossil Evidence of Evolution

Most of what we know about ancient organisms comes from the fossil record. The fossil record provides evidence about the history of life and past environments on Earth. The fossil record also shows how different groups of organisms have changed over time. Each new discovery helps to fill holes in our understanding of evolution.

Early Earth When Earth first formed, more than 4.5 billion years ago, it was extremely hot. Earth was likely mostly melted. As Earth cooled, solid rocks became stable at Earth's surface. The oldest known fossils are from rocks that formed about a billion years after Earth formed. **Figure 4** shows a rock made of these fossils. Scientists think that all other forms of life on Earth arose from these simple organisms.

Scientists cannot yet pinpoint when or where life first evolved. Scientists hypothesize that life first evolved in Earth's ocean. The early ocean contained reactive chemicals. Under the right conditions, sunlight and lightning can change those chemicals into molecules similar to those found in living cells. More research will help scientists to settle the question of the origin of life on Earth.

Fossils Reveal Early Life
Figure 4 Stromatolites are rock-like structures formed by layers of fossilized bacteria. Dating as far back as 3.4 billion years ago, they are the oldest evidence of life forms on Earth. Ancient bacteria in water produced thin sheets of film that trapped mud. Over time, these thin sheets formed microfossils—fossils too small to see without a microscope. Eventually, the sheets built up into the layers you see here.

Interpret Photos ✏ Using evidence in the picture, determine the oldest and youngest layers. Then, draw a vertical scale next to the stromatolite to show which are the oldest layers and which are the youngest.

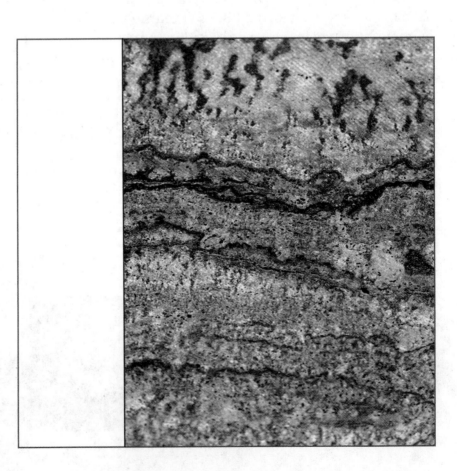

Gomphotherium
24–5 mya

Moeritherium
36 mya

Platybelodon
23–5.3 mya

Mammut americanum
(American mastodon)
4 mya–11,500 ya

Mammuthus
(Woolly Mammoth)
Pliocene, from
750,000–11,500 ya

Loxodonta
(African elephant)
1.8 mya–present

ya = years ago; mya = millions of years ago

Fossils and Evolution Through Time The fossil record provides evidence that life on Earth has evolved. Rock forms in layers, with newer layers on top of older layers. When we dig deeper, we see older rocks with fossils from earlier time periods. The oldest rocks contain fossils of only very simple organisms. Younger rocks include fossils of both simple organisms and also more complex organisms. Scientists also place fossils in chronological order using radioactive dating, which uses radioactive isotopes of elements to assign an age range to a fossil. Looking at fossils in rocks from different time periods, scientists can reconstruct the history of evolution. **Figure 5** shows the evolution of the elephant, reconstructed from the fossil record.

The fossil record also shows how Earth's climate has changed. Some plant fossils reveal surprises, such as palm trees in Wyoming and giant tropical ferns in Antarctica. Fossils and preserved remains are also evidence of how climate change influences evolution.

Evolution of the Modern Elephant
Figure 5 Scientists have reconstructed the evolutionary history of the elephant with evidence from the fossil record.

✓CHECK POINT **Cite Textual Evidence** Would you expect to find fossils related to the evolution of the elephant in the oldest rocks in the fossil record? Explain.

....

....

....

....

Question It!

Kyle has very limited vision and needs someone to explain the evolution of elephants to him. Suppose you are going to work with Kyle to help him understand the changes elephants have undergone.

Interpret Diagrams Using **Figure 5**, what features of the animals have stayed the same? What features have changed?

....

....

....

....

....

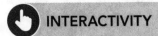
Comparisons of Anatomy

The structure of an organism's body is called its anatomy. Similarities in anatomy between organisms from the fossil record and organisms living today are clues they evolved from a common ancestor. These clues include similarities in embryological development. They help us to reconstruct evolutionary history.

Embryological Development An **embryo** is a young organism that develops from a fertilized egg (called a zygote). The growing embryo may develop inside or outside the parent's body. The early development of different organisms in an embryo shows some striking similarities that are not present in the fully developed organisms. For example, chickens, fish, turtles, and pigs all resemble each other during the early stages of development. Anatomical similarities in early development suggest that organisms are related and share a common ancestor.

Scientists can also analyze fossilized eggs to infer lines of descent. **Figure 6** shows the model of a duck-billed dinosaur embryo, known as a hadrosaur, compared to an x-ray of a chicken embryo. You can see many anatomical similarities in their early development.

Homologous Structures Similar structures that related species have inherited from a common ancestor are known as **homologous structures** (hoh MAHL uh gus). Bats, dogs, dolphins, and even flying reptiles have homologous structures in their limbs. Although the structures look very different now, the Math Toolbox shows you the bones that these animals all have in common.

Birds and Dinosaurs

Figure 6 ✎ Draw lines and label the features that look similar in both the hadrosaur and chicken embryos.

Hadrosaur

Chicken

Homologous Anatomical Structures

The wings, flipper, and leg of these organisms all have similar anatomical (body) structures. Note that the structures are not drawn to scale.

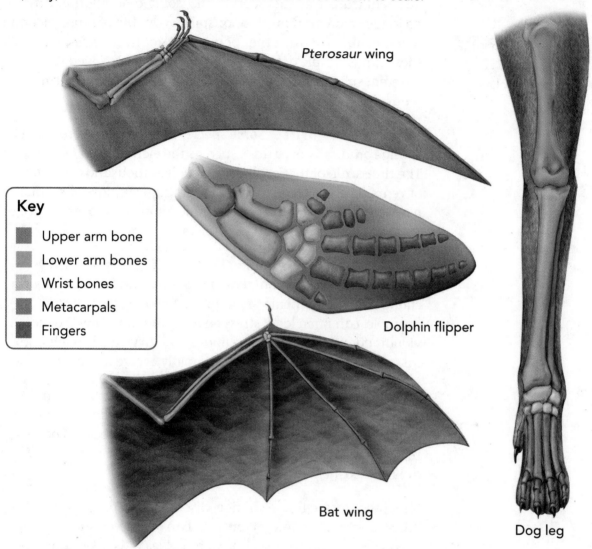

Key

- ■ Upper arm bone
- ■ Lower arm bones
- ■ Wrist bones
- ■ Metacarpals
- ■ Fingers

Pterosaur wing

Dolphin flipper

Bat wing

Dog leg

1. **Construct Tables** 🖊 Choose two of the animals shown above to examine closely. Using a metric ruler, measure the upper arm bone, the lower arm bone, and the fingers. Create a data table to the right and record the measurements in millimeters.

2. **CCC Analyze Proportional Relationships** In each species, compare the upper arm to lower arm, or compare fingers to metacarpals. Can you find any equivalent ratios?

....

....

....

....

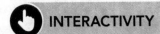

INTERACTIVITY

Interpret data from the fossil record that supports species extinction.

VIDEO

Find evidence for evolution in the fossil record.

Beginning and End of a Species

Natural selection explains how variations can lead to changes in a species. A new species forms when one population remains isolated from the rest of its species long enough to evolve such different traits that members of the isolated population can no longer mate and produce offspring capable of reproduction with members of any other populations of the species. **Figure 7** shows an example of a turtle species that has evolved seven different subspecies. Over time, the subspecies could form separate species.

Gradual Change Some species in the fossil record seem to change gradually over time, such as the elephants in **Figure 5**. The time scale of the fossil record involves thousands or millions of years. There is plenty of time for gradual changes to produce new species. The fossil record contains many examples of species that are halfway between two others.

Rapid Change At times, new, related species suddenly appear in the fossil record. Rapid evolution can follow a major change in environmental conditions. A cooling climate, for example, can put a lot of stress on a population. Only the individuals adapted to cooler conditions will survive. Through natural selection, the population may rapidly evolve to a new species.

Extinction A species is **extinct** if it no longer exists and will never again live on Earth. A rapid environmental change is more likely to cause extinction than a new species. The fossil record shows that most of the species that ever lived on Earth are now extinct.

New predators, climate change, disease, and competition with other species are a few factors that can lead to extinction. According to natural selection, if a species fails to develop the adaptations necessary to survive the changing conditions in an environment, that species will not survive and reproduce. Small populations that breed slowly and cannot relocate are more likely to become extinct. The fossil record shows that volcanic eruptions, asteroids striking Earth, and sudden climate change can kill off many species in a short time.

✓ CHECK POINT **Translate Information** How do you know that the animals whose limbs are depicted in the Math Toolbox had a common ancestor at one point? What question could you ask to find out more and why would you ask it?

....

....

....

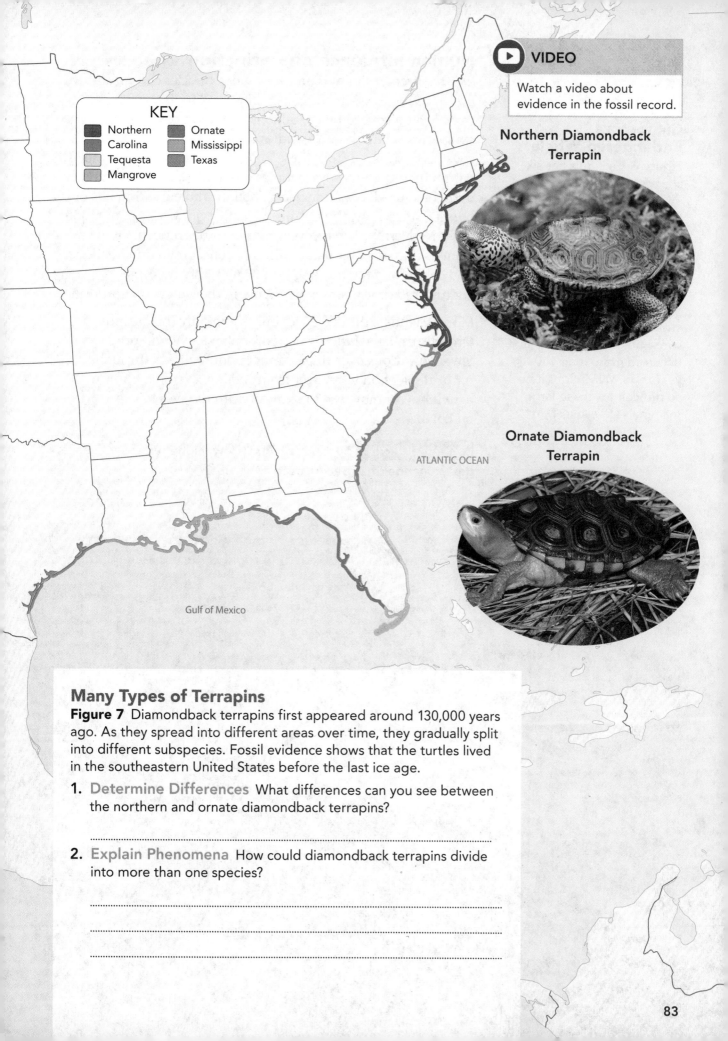

▶ VIDEO

Watch a video about evidence in the fossil record.

KEY

■	Northern	■	Ornate
■	Carolina	■	Mississippi
■	Tequesta	■	Texas
■	Mangrove		

ATLANTIC OCEAN

Gulf of Mexico

Northern Diamondback Terrapin

Ornate Diamondback Terrapin

Many Types of Terrapins

Figure 7 Diamondback terrapins first appeared around 130,000 years ago. As they spread into different areas over time, they gradually split into different subspecies. Fossil evidence shows that the turtles lived in the southeastern United States before the last ice age.

1. **Determine Differences** What differences can you see between the northern and ornate diamondback terrapins?

   ....

2. **Explain Phenomena** How could diamondback terrapins divide into more than one species?

   ....

   ....

   ....

California's Endangered Whales

Figure 8 California has six species of whales on the endangered species list: the north Pacific right, blue, sei, fin, humpback, and the sperm whale.

SEP Cite Textual Evidence

Some species of whale have struggled to overcome over-hunting by humans that occurred more than 100 years ago. Why might it be so difficult for these large mammals to recover?

....

....

....

....

Human Influence on Extinction

Some extinctions are the direct result of human activities. Species cannot survive over-hunting, sudden climate change, and indirect changes to their habitat caused by the actions of human communities. The six species of endangered whales on North America's Pacific coast have suffered from these kinds of changes. As they move within their habitat, some whales are hunted, injured by ships, and are injured in fishing gear. Though whale hunting has been banned since 1949, the northern Pacific right whale population is not recovering. The recovery plan includes reducing injuries from fishing gear, reducing ship collisions, protecting habitats, and continuing the hunting ban. **Figure 8** shows three endangered species of whales living in the waters off California.

Many scientists think extinctions are rapidly increasing. Organisms like whales, who reproduce slowly and produce fewer variations over time, cannot adapt quickly through natural selection to recover from sudden, extreme human activities. We may lose the largest animals ever to live on Earth.

✓ CHECK POINT **Summarize Text** How might humans influence the extinction of a species, such as whales?

....

humpback whale

sperm whale

blue whale

☑ LESSON 4 Check

MS-LS4-1, MS-LS4-2, MS-LS4-3, MS-LS4-6, EP&CIIa

1. **Infer** Refer to the figure **Birds and Dinosaurs**. If two organisms have homologous structures and similar early development, what can you infer about them?

....

....

2. **SEP Analyze Data** According to the fossil record, which level in the rock layers shown in the diagram will have the oldest organisms? Explain.

....

....

....

....

....

....

3. **SEP Construct Explanations** How do you account for differences between the bat's wing and the dolphin's flipper?

....

....

....

Dolphin flipper

Bat wing

4. **SEP Engage in Argument** What can you say to back the claim that the fossil record supports the theory of evolution?

....

....

....

....

5. **CCC Describe Patterns** If you were a scientist trying to determine if an organism evolved gradually or rapidly, how would patterns in the fossil record help you? Explain how the pattern would provide evidence to support the rate of evolution for that organism.

....

....

....

....

....

....

....

....

....

....

6. **Apply Scientific Reasoning** Why is a sudden change in the environment more likely to cause a species to go extinct rather than to cause a new species to develop?

....

....

....

....

....

....

....

5 Other Evidence of Evolution

uInvestigate Explore how DNA provides evidence for evolution.

MS-LS4-2 Apply scientific ideas to construct an explanation for the anatomical similarities and differences among modern organisms and between modern and fossil organisms to infer evolutionary relationships.

MS-LS4-6 Use mathematical representations to support explanations of how natural selection may lead to increases and decreases of specific traits in populations over time.

Connect It !

✏ **Count the number of different kinds of organisms you see and write your number in the white circle on the photograph.**

SEP Evaluate Evidence What do all the organisms in the photo have in common, and what does this suggest about how closely related they are to one another?

....

....

....

Using Technology to Study Evolution

Advances in technology have led to new knowledge about evolution. Darwin and scientists of his time used their eyes, hand tools, and simple microscopes to study evolution. Darwin's microscope had less than 200x magnification. Modern scientists have much better tools. We now have such powerful microscopes and imaging devices that computers can show us the shapes of individual molecules. Future advances may further our understanding of evolution.

Genetic Material and Evolution The coral reef in **Figure 1** contains an amazing variety of living things. The diverse shapes, body structures, and lifestyles are all due to differences in genetic material, the set of chemical instructions that guide the function and growth of an organism. Evolution results from changes in genetic material. Small changes in genetic material lead to microevolution within species. An accumulation of small changes causes macroevolution, or the creation of new species.

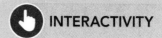

INTERACTIVITY

Discuss how a device or object you use every day has changed over time.

Literacy Connection

Read and Comprehend
As you work your way through this lesson, stop frequently to see if you understand what you just read. Each paragraph has key information. Try to restate it in your own words.

Rainbow of Life on a Reef
Figure 1 All of the differences among the organisms in this coral reef at Anacapa Island, California result from evolutionary changes in genetic material.

Genetic Evidence for a Common Ancestor

Every living thing uses DNA for genetic material. Mosquitoes, humans, plants, and bacteria all have cells with the same system of genetic material. The shared use of DNA is one piece of evidence that every organism on Earth has a common ancestor. This common ancestor, called LUCA for Last Universal Common Ancestor, was most likely a single-celled organism similar to modern bacteria or archaea.

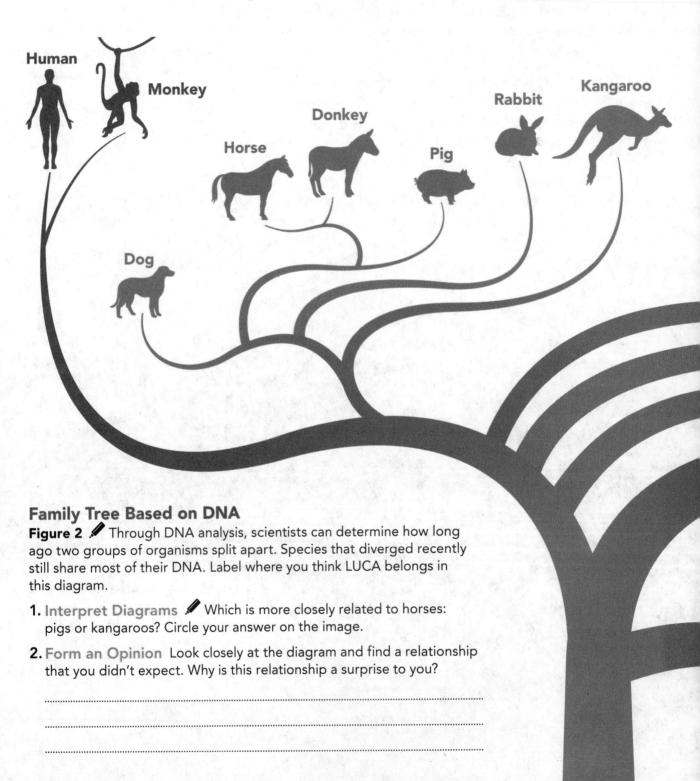

Family Tree Based on DNA

Figure 2 Through DNA analysis, scientists can determine how long ago two groups of organisms split apart. Species that diverged recently still share most of their DNA. Label where you think LUCA belongs in this diagram.

1. **Interpret Diagrams** Which is more closely related to horses: pigs or kangaroos? Circle your answer on the image.

2. **Form an Opinion** Look closely at the diagram and find a relationship that you didn't expect. Why is this relationship a surprise to you?

....

....

....

Dawn of Evolution DNA is a complex molecule, difficult to copy without making any mistakes. LUCA started to change as it accumulated mutations, or changes to its DNA. Natural selection and other processes shaped LUCA's evolution. The original population of LUCA split and diverged, evolving into all the species that live or have ever lived on Earth. The traces of this evolution are recorded in the DNA of every organism. Shared DNA between species provides evidence of the evolutionary past. The more similar the DNA between two species, the more closely related they are. **Figure 2** shows a family tree based on differences in one stretch of DNA.

HANDS-ON LAB

И**Investigate** Explore how DNA provides evidence for evolution.

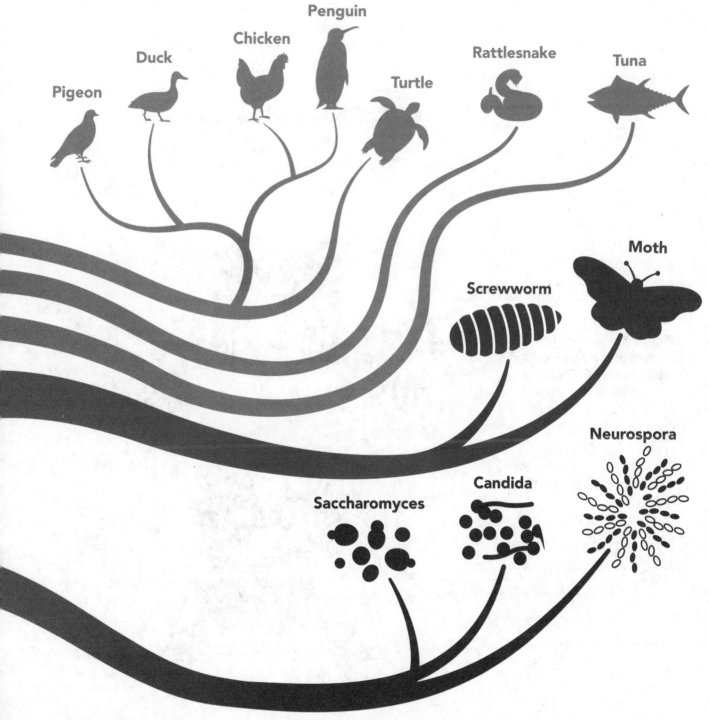

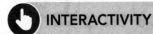

INTERACTIVITY

Explore how different types of evidence help to establish evolutionary relationships.

VIDEO

Learn about a career in evolutionary biology.

Proteins Recall that genes code for different **proteins**, which are complicated molecules that carry out important cellular functions. Proteins can act as the building blocks for cell materials and carry out important cellular functions. For example, some muscle fibers are made of chains of the protein actin. Other proteins act as messengers, fight diseases, carry out chemical reactions, or carry materials around the body.

Proteins and Evolution Consider what could happen to the function of a protein if the gene for it contains a mutation. The mutant genetic material may code for a different form of the protein, as shown in **Figure 3**. The new version of the protein may increase the individual's fitness. More likely, the mutation will lower the individual's fitness or leave it unchanged. Changes in proteins lead to variations within a population. Natural selection acts on those variations, causing evolution.

✓ CHECK POINT **Determine Central Ideas** What are the possible effects of a mutation on the function of a protein?

....

....

Mutations and Proteins

Figure 3 The Mre11-Rad50 protein group helps cells to repair breaks in DNA molecules. There is only a small mutation in the genetic code for the bottom form.

Determine Differences How are the two forms of the protein group different?

....

....

....

....

....

....

....

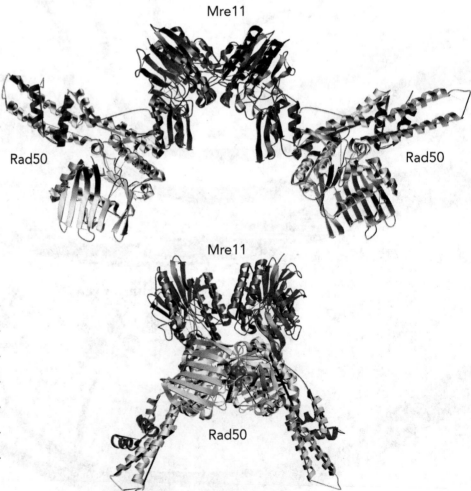

Protein Analysis and Evolution Scientists compare proteins to see how closely two species are related. In most cases, evidence from DNA and protein structure confirms conclusions based on fossils, embryos, and body structure. For example, DNA comparisons show that dogs are more similar to wolves than to coyotes. This confirms an earlier conclusion based on similarities in the structure and development of the three species.

▶ VIDEO

Watch a video about other evidence of evolution.

📓 **Student Discourse** On your own, consider the data in the Math Toolbox table. Then use mathematical expressions to decide which two primate groups likely have the least traits in common with each other. Then in a small group, compare and discuss your answers and the supporting math.

Math Toolbox

All in the Family

Humans, apes, and monkeys are all members of the order Primates. Bonobos, chimpanzees, gorillas, and orangutans are all considered apes, but monkeys are not. Humans and monkeys share about 93 percent of their DNA.

Primate	Genetic Difference with Humans
Bonobo	1.2%
Chimpanzee	1.3%
Gorilla	1.6%
Orangutan	3.1%
Monkey	7.0%

1. **Use Algebraic Expressions** Write an expression representing the percentage of DNA that gorillas share with humans. Let g = gorilla.

....

....

2. **Draw Comparative Inferences** What can you say about the evolutionary relationship between the apes and monkeys compared to humans?

....

....

☑ LESSON 5 Check

1. **SEP Provide Evidence** What evidence is there that every organism on Earth shares a common ancestor?

....

....

2. **Compare and Contrast** What do microevolution and macroevolution have in common? How do they differ?

....

....

....

....

....

3. **Synthesize Information** How have advances in technology supported the theory of evolution?

....

....

....

....

....

4. **SEP Use Mathematics** Refer to the data table in the Math Toolbox. Given that natural selection acts on variations and influences evolution, which two primate groups would you expect to have the most traits in common? Support your answer with a mathematical expression.

....

....

....

....

5. **Support Your Explanation** What does LUCA stand for and how did it evolve into all the life forms we see today?

....

....

....

....

....

....

....

Quest CHECK-IN

In this lesson, you learned more about how genetics drives evolution and how mutations to proteins lead to variations within a population.

CCC Cause and Effect What caused changes to the blackcap populations? How was natural selection at work here?

....

....

....

....

👆 INTERACTIVITY

Prepare Your Report

Go online to investigate the European blackcaps. Look for new information to add to your report. Brainstorm ideas for different ways to represent information.

MS-LS4-2, MS-LS4-4, MS-LS4-5

DNA, Fossils, and Evolution

All living things contain DNA. This blueprint carries the codes for every trait an organism expresses. We now have the technology to extract DNA from living things, as well as fossils, and then map out the locations of all the genes. By comparing modern DNA with that of fossils, it is possible to determine which traits similar species have in common.

Scientists are able to remove and analyze DNA from fossils using a process called an assay. DNA is removed from the center of a fossil and then prepared using an assortment of different chemicals. The DNA sample is then amplified and run through a process called gel electrophoresis. This separates different pieces of the DNA. The results are then compared to known DNA to see how similar they are.

One of the interesting things DNA research has discovered is that the domestication of dogs has changed their diet. While ancestral wolves ate mostly meat, modern dogs have more genes to help them digest starch and other carbohydrates. This suggests that the early dogs who could handle the starches in the human diet had an advantage.

MY DISCOVERY

With a classmate, research how dogs were domesticated from wolves. Engage in a classroom debate about the evidence that supports and refutes the descent of dogs from wolves.

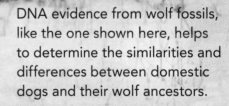

DNA evidence from wolf fossils, like the one shown here, helps to determine the similarities and differences between domestic dogs and their wolf ancestors.

93

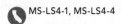

MS-LS4-1, MS-LS4-4

Evidence-Based Assessment

A group of scientists was researching evolutionary relationships. They decided to investigate a particular protein called cytochrome-c. Proteins are made up of compounds called amino acids. They compared the amino acid sequence that codes for the protein among several species. They made a surprising discovery. In moths, whales, and baker's yeast—organisms that do not look at all related—almost half of the positions in the cytochrome-c amino acid sequence were identical.

Cytochrome-c is a very important protein when it comes to releasing energy from food. Like other proteins, cytochrome-c is made of a sequence of amino acids that may or may not vary among organisms. The analysis of cytochrome-c in different organisms provides strong evidence for determining which organisms are closely related. Scientists can predict evolutionary relationships by looking at the amino acid sequences in cytochrome-c that different organisms have in common.

The data table shows ten positions where there are different amino acids in the sequence that codes for the cytochrome-c protein from five different species. In all other positions, the amino acids are the same.

Species	Amino Acid, Position Number in Sequence									
	20	23	52	55	66	68	70	91	97	100
human	M	S	P	S	I	G	D	V	E	A
horse	Q	A	P	S	T	L	E	A	T	E
kangaroo	Q	A	P	T	I	G	D	A	G	A
pig	Q	A	P	S	T	G	E	A	G	E
whale	Q	A	V	S	T	G	E	A	G	A

SOURCE: National Center for Biotechnology Information

Amino Acid Symbols

A = Alanine   M = Methionine

D = Aspartic Acid   P = Proline

E = Glutamic Acid   Q = Glutamine

G = Glycine   S = Serine

I = Isoleucine   T = Threonine

L = Lysine   V = Valine

1. **SEP Analyze Data** According to cytochrome-c analysis, to which other species is the horse most closely related?

A. human   B. pig

C. kangaroo   D. whale

2. **Support Your Explanation** How did you determine the horse's closest relation among the four species? Use evidence from the data table to support your claim.

....

....

....

....

....

....

....

....

....

....

....

....

....

....

3. **SEP Cite Evidence** Complete the table below to compare the number of different amino acids among the five organisms. Based on the table, circle the organism that is least like the human. Underline the organism that is most like the human.

Organism	Number of Shared Amino Acids with Humans
horse	
kangaroo	
pig	
whale	

4. **SEP Construct Explanations** Cows and sheep have the same sequence of amino acids in their cytochrome-c protein. How is it possible that they can be different species? Select all that apply.

☐ This is the result of convergent evolution.

☐ These two species share a recent common ancestor.

☐ They evolved under different environmental pressures.

☐ They are not closely related.

☐ Similar sequences of cytochrome-c protein do not indicate relatedness.

Quest FINDINGS

Complete the Quest!

Create a multimedia report about the two populations of European blackcaps and what caused them to be so different from each other.

Draw Conclusions If evolution of the blackcaps continues at the current rate, what can be said about similarities of the populations of European blackcaps to their common ancestor and to one another?

....

....

....

....

INTERACTIVITY

Reflect on Blackcap Migration

MS-LS4-2, MS-LS4-4

A Bony
Puzzle

How can you analyze **patterns** in structures to **show** evolutionary **relationships?**

Background

Phenomenon A new museum of natural history is opening in your community. The director of the museum has asked your class to help with an exhibit about evolutionary history. The director hopes you can show how patterns in skeletons provide clues about common ancestors.

In this investigation, you will analyze and compare the internal and external structures of a pigeon, a bat, and a rabbit. Then you will use the similarities and differences you observe to describe a possible common ancestor and infer evolutionary relationships among these organisms.

Materials

(per group)

• Activity Sheets 1, 2, and 3
• ruler

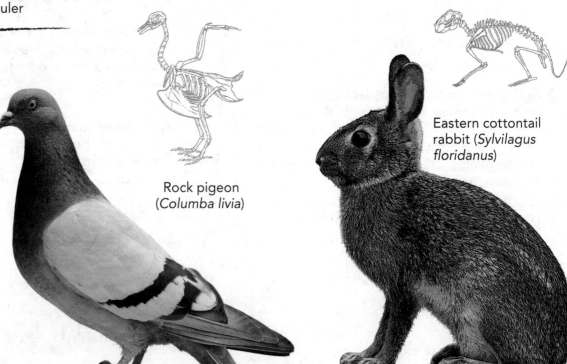

Eastern cottontail rabbit (*Sylvilagus floridanus*)

Rock pigeon
(*Columba livia*)

Indian flying fox (*Pteropus giganteus*)

Plan Your Investigation

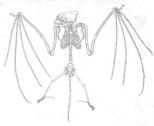

1. Using the photographs and the diagrams, you will compare the features and structures of the pigeon, bat, and rabbit. You will look for patterns in the skeletons and note similarities and differences among the three animals.

2. Work with your group to plan a procedure for comparing the skeletons of the three animals. Write out your plan in the space provided. Consider the following questions as a guide for planning your procedure:

   - Should we compare all the bones shown in the diagrams or select a few important features that they all have in common to compare?

   - Do we also want to include our observations from the photographs of the animals?

   - What's the best way to record and organize our observations so we can analyze them more easily? Should we write notes summarizing what we see? Or should we use only data tables to organize the data?

3. After receiving your teacher's approval, follow the procedure your group developed. Remember that you may need to revise the plan as you carry it out. Record your observations about the three skeletons in the data tables.

HANDS-ON LAB

Demonstrate Go online for a downloadable worksheet of this lab.

Procedure

Observations

Skeleton	Similarities	Differences
Spine		
Skull		
Limbs		

Photos	Similarities	Differences
covering		
faces		
other		

Analyze and Interpret Data

1. **CCC Identify Patterns** What evidence did you find that will help you describe how these three skeletons are alike?

   ....
   ....
   ....
   ....

2. **SEP Evaluate Evidence** How does the skeleton pattern that you identified provide evidence for a common ancestor among the pigeon, bat, and rabbit?

   ....
   ....
   ....

3. **Explain Phenomena** Which bones of the common ancestor do you think might have changed the most in its descendants? Which bones remained about the same? Cite evidence from the skeleton diagrams to support your answer.

   ....
   ....
   ....
   ....

4. **CCC Structure and Function** How are the wings of the bat and the bird, and the rabbit's front legs, all examples of homologous structures? Use evidence from your investigation to support your answer.

   ....
   ....
   ....
   ....

5. **SEP Construct Explanations** The museum exhibit will include information to explain evolutionary relationships. What evidence can you use to show that bats share a more recent common ancestor with rabbits than they do with birds?

   ....
   ....
   ....

History of Earth

Investigative Phenomenon
What evidence can be used to construct a history of Earth's past?

MS-ESS1-4 Construct a scientific explanation based on evidence from rock strata for how the geologic time scale is used to organize Earth's 4.6-billion-year-old history.

EP&CIIc Students should be developing an understanding that the expansion and operation of human communities influences the geographic extent, composition, biological diversity, and viability of natural systems.

EP&CVa Students should be developing an understanding of the spectrum of what is considered in making decisions about resources and natural systems and how those factors influence decisions.

HANDS-ON LAB

иConnect Develop a timeline of the major events in the life of a family member.

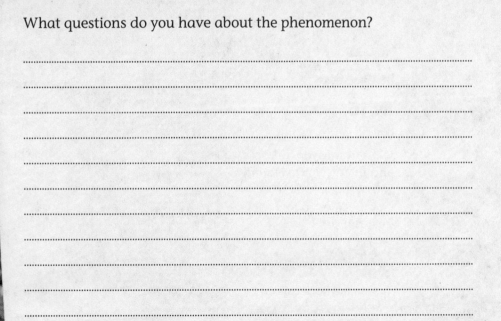

What do these fossils reveal about Earth's past?

What questions do you have about the phenomenon?

....
....
....
....
....
....
....
....
....

Quest PBL

How do paleontologists know where to look for fossils?

Figure It Out Dr. Digg is the head paleontologist at a museum. She has hired you to help the museum set up a new exhibit on an extinct genus of ancient animal called *Dimetrodon*. Where in the world can you find *Dimetrodon* fossils to form the centerpiece of the exhibit? Fossils are found all over Earth, and you can't dig up the entire planet. In this problem-based Quest activity, you will choose a dig site that is likely to produce fossils of *Dimetrodon*. You will evaluate information about four sites, using information about rock layers and other fossils found at those sites to narrow the choices down. In a final report, you will share your evaluations of each site and give reasons for choosing one site and rejecting the other three.

NBC LEARN ▶ VIDEO

After viewing the Quest Kickoff video and watching a paleontologist at work, complete the concept map by recording four things that you should consider when exploring for fossils.

How to Find Fossils

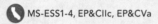 MS-ESS1-4, EP&CIIc, EP&CVa

👆 **INTERACTIVITY**

The Big Fossil Hunt

Quest CHECK-INS

IN LESSON 1

What do paleontologists learn from layers of rock and the organisms found within those layers? Gather clues to find the best dig site.

👆 **INTERACTIVITY**

Clues in the Rock Layers

👆 **INTERACTIVITY**

Fossils Around the World

Quest CHECK-IN

IN LESSON 2

How do paleontologists use the geologic time scale to help find fossils? Explore how scientists use information from already-discovered fossils to predict where other fossils might be.

🧪 **HANDS-ON LAB**

A Matter of Time

This preserved dire wolf skeleton represents one of the over 4,000 unearthed remains from a now extinct species. The wolves were trapped in the La Brea Tar Pits in Los Angeles, California. Fossils dug from the tar pits are as old as 55,000 years.

Quest CHECK-IN

IN LESSON 3

How do paleontologists use information about ancient organisms to determine where to search for fossils? Conduct research and make a final selection of a dig site for *Dimetrodon*.

👆 **INTERACTIVITY**

Time to Choose the Dig Site

Quest FINDINGS

Complete the Quest!

Prepare a report in which you evaluate each site and give reasons for choosing or rejecting that site.

👆 **INTERACTIVITY**

Reflect on the Big Fossil Hunt

Determining Ages of Rocks

и**Investigate** Model changes in rocks.

MS-ESS1-4 Construct a scientific explanation based on evidence from rock strata for how the geologic time scale is used to organize Earth's 4.6-billion-year-old history.

Connect It!

✏ **How many rock layers do you see? Draw an arrow pointing from the youngest rock to the oldest rock.**

SEP Construct Explanations How did you decide which rocks are the youngest and oldest?

....

....

....

Apply Scientific Reasoning Suppose you were the first person to study the canyon. How could you find out exactly how old the oldest rock is?

....

....

....

Describing the Ages of Rocks

If you visit the Painted Desert in Arizona, you will find rock layers that look gray, red, green, blue, and even purple. If you're curious, you might start by asking "How did these colorful rocks form?" Your next question would probably be "How old are these rocks?" In other words, you would want to describe the ages of the rocks. Geologists have two ways to describe the age of a rock: age **relative** to another rock, and age in number of years since the rock formed.

Relative Age
The **relative age** of a rock is its age compared to the ages of other rocks. You probably use the idea of relative age when you compare your age with someone else's. For example, if you say that you are older than your brother but younger than your sister, you describe your relative age.

Absolute Age
The relative age of a rock does not provide its absolute age. The **absolute age** of a rock is the number of years that have passed since the rock formed. It may be impossible to know the exact absolute age of some rocks, so geologists often use both absolute and relative ages.

Why do geologists want to analyze and describe the ages of rocks? Evidence of past events occurs in rocks. That evidence shows that Earth has changed and evolved over time due to natural processes. Rock layers like those in **Figure 1** form a record of Earth's history of change, known as the *geologic record*. By studying clues in Earth's rocks and determining their ages, geologists can organize past events in sequence to better understand Earth's history.

✓ CHECK POINT **Summarize Text** What is the difference between relative age and absolute age?

....
....
....

Academic Vocabulary
Describe your location relative to an object or another person in the room.

....
....
....

Rainbow of Rock Layers
Figure 1 Many colorful rock layers make up the hills of Arizona's Painted Desert. These rock layers represent many millions of years of Earth's history.

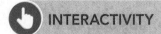
INTERACTIVITY

Examine a sequence of rock layers to learn their relative ages.

Determining Relative Ages of Rocks

Geologists use many methods to determine the age of Earth's rocks. To find a rock's relative age, they analyze the position of rock layers. They also look for a variety of clues in rocks, such as fossils. These methods provide ways to find relative ages, but not absolute ages, of rocks and fossils found within the rocks.

Clues Within Rocks

Figure 2 🖉 Intrusions and faults can help to determine a sequence of events within rock layers.

1. Identify Knowns Draw an *X* over the igneous intrusion. Draw a line along a fault.

2. CCC Patterns 🖉 The rock layers are (older / younger) than any faults or intrusions that run through them.

3. Synthesize Information The San Andreas fault runs for hundreds of miles through California. What occurs when rocks on either side of the fault move?

Position of Rock Layers Sedimentary rock usually forms in horizontal layers, or strata. Geologists use the **law of superposition** to determine the relative ages of sedimentary rock layers. According to the law of superposition, in undisturbed horizontal sedimentary rock layers, the oldest layer is at the bottom and the youngest layer is at the top. The higher you go, the younger the rocks are. The lower or deeper you go, the older the rocks are.

Clues from Igneous Rocks Magma is molten material beneath Earth's surface. Lava (magma that reaches the surface) can harden on the surface to form an igneous extrusion. Magma can also push into layers of rock below the surface. The magma can harden and form an igneous intrusion, like the one shown in **Figure 2**. An extrusion is younger than the rock it covers. An intrusion is younger than the rock around it.

Clues from Faults More clues come from the study of faults. A fault, like the one shown in **Figure 2**, is a break in Earth's crust. Forces inside Earth cause movement of the rock on opposite sides of a fault. A fault is always younger than the rock it cuts through. To determine the relative age of a fault, geologists find the relative age of the youngest layer cut by the fault.

Igneous Intrusion

Faults

Using Fossils The preserved remains or traces of living things are called **fossils**. They most often occur in layers of sedimentary rock. Fossils preserved in rock layers provide physical evidence about the existence, diversity, and change in lifeforms throughout the history of life on Earth and how Earth has changed over time.

Certain fossils, called index fossils, help geologists to match and date rock layers, even if those layers are far apart or in different locations. An index fossil is a fossil of an organism that was widely distributed and existed for a geologically short period of time. Fossils from organisms that lived for a long geologic time might show up in multiple rock layers, but index fossils show up in only a few layers. Index fossils are useful because they tell the relative ages of the rock layers in which they occur. Geologists **infer** that layers with matching index fossils are the same age.

You can use index fossils to match rock layers and find their relative ages. Look at the diagram in **Figure 3,** which shows rock layers from four different locations. Notice that two of the fossils are found in only one rock layer. These are index fossils.

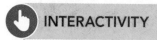
INTERACTIVITY

Use index fossils to decode Earth's history.

Academic Vocabulary

Think about a pet you saw recently. What can you infer about the animal's age? Explain your answer.

....

....

....

....

Model It

Using Fossils to Match Rock Layers
Figure 3 You can model how scientists use index fossils to match rock layers separated by distance.

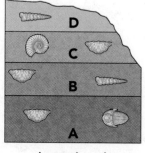 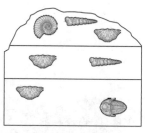 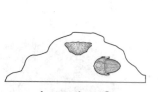 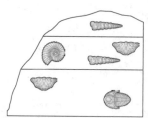

Location 1   Location 2   Location 3   Location 4

1. **Interpret Diagrams** 🖋 At Location 1, circle the fossils that you can use as index fossils.

2. **SEP Use Models** 🖋 Use the index fossils at Location 1 to label the matching layers at Locations 2–4. Then, draw a line to connect each matching layer across all locations.

3. **CCC Patterns** At Location 4, what can you infer the geologic history and the ages of the rock layers? Cite evidence to support your inference.

....

....

Changes in Rocks

The geologic record of sedimentary rock layers is not complete. In fact, erosion destroyed most of Earth's geologic record over billions of years. Gaps in the geologic record and folding can change the position in which rock layers appear. As was shown in **Figure 2**, motion along faults can also change how rock layers line up. These changes make it harder for scientists to reconstruct Earth's history. **Figure 4** shows how the order of rock layers may change.

Gaps in the Geologic Record

When rock layers erode, an older rock surface may be exposed. Then deposition begins again, building new rock layers. The surface where new rock layers meet a much older rock surface beneath them is called an unconformity. An **unconformity** is a gap in the geologic record. It shows where rock layers have been lost due to erosion.

Folding

Sometimes, forces inside Earth fold rock layers so much that the layers are turned over completely. In this case, the youngest rock layers may be on the bottom!

Samples from many different areas are needed to give a complete geologic record. Geologists compare rock layers in many places to understand a complete sequence.

☑ CHECK POINT **Write Explanatory Texts** In your own words, explain one of the methods that geologists use to find the relative ages of rocks.

....

....

....

Literacy Connection

Write Explanatory Texts Underline the sentences in the text that explain how the rock layers in **Figure 4** changed.

Unconformity and Folding

Figure 4 🖊 Shade the oldest and youngest layers in the last two diagrams. Label the unconformity. Circle the part of the fold that is overturned.

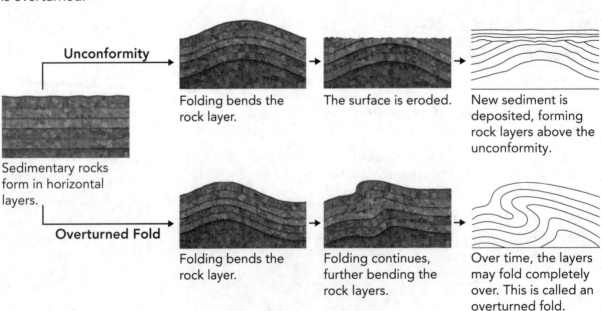

Sedimentary rocks form in horizontal layers.

Unconformity

Folding bends the rock layer.

The surface is eroded.

New sediment is deposited, forming rock layers above the unconformity.

Overturned Fold

Folding bends the rock layer.

Folding continues, further bending the rock layers.

Over time, the layers may fold completely over. This is called an overturned fold.

MS-ESS1-4

1. **Apply Concepts** How could a geologist match the rock layers in one area to rock layers found in another area?

....

....

....

....

2. **CCC Patterns** A layer of sandstone sits above two other layers of rock. A fault cuts through the two lower layers of rock. How does the age of the fault compare with the ages of all three rock layers?

....

....

....

....

....

....

....

3. **SEP Construct Explanations** A geologist observes rock layers that are folded. She determines that a layer of siltstone is younger than the layer of limestone above it. How can you explain the geologist's findings?

....

....

....

....

....

....

....

....

....

....

....

....

....

Quest CHECK-INS

In this lesson, you learned how geologists find the ages of rocks and how events and fossil histories are recorded within the rock layers.

Explain How can information from rock layers give you clues about where to look for additional fossils?

....

....

....

....

INTERACTIVITIES

- Clues in the Rock Layers
- Fossils Around the World

Go online to think about the layers of rock at the dig sites and to consider how knowing more about the ages of rocks and fossils can help you to choose where to look for another fossil.

Geologic Time Scale

ɴInvestigate Model the geologic time scale.

MS-ESS1-4 Construct a scientific explanation based on evidence from rock strata for how the geologic time scale is used to organize Earth's 4.6-billion-year-old history.

Connect It!

✏ **Circle the unconformity. What does it tell you about the history of this location?**

Interpret Photos What can you infer about the history based on these rocks?

....

....

CCC Patterns How could you use the information in these rocks to organize events in Earth's history?

....

....

The Geologic Time Scale

When you speak of the past, what names do you use for different spans of time? You probably use names such as *century, decade, year, month, week,* and *day.* But these units aren't very helpful for thinking about much longer periods of time—such as the 4.6 billion years of Earth's history.

To **organize** this vast number of years into manageable periods, scientists created the geologic time scale. The **geologic time scale** is a record of the geologic events and the evolution of life forms as shown in the rock and fossil records. Notice that the geologic time scale in **Figure 2** is a timeline—a model of the relative order of events over a long period of time that might otherwise be difficult to study.

Scientists first developed the geologic time scale by studying rock layers and index fossils worldwide. They gathered evidence using methods of determining the relative ages of rocks, such as evidence from unconformities as in **Figure 1**. With this evidence, scientists placed Earth's rocks in order by relative age. Later, they used other methods to help them determine the absolute age of the divisions in the geologic time scale.

✓ **CHECK POINT** **Summarize Text** How do scientists organize Earth's history, and what evidence do they use?

....

....

....

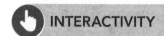

INTERACTIVITY

Consider the best way to represent the geologic time scale.

Academic Vocabulary

Describe how you organize something in your life. Compare the state of that thing before and after you organized it.

....

....

....

....

....

A Gap in Time
Figure 1 This unconformity is in a roadside cliff that runs through the San Andreas fault near Palmdale, California. Unconformities represent gaps in geologic time.

The Geologic Time Scale

Figure 2 The geologic time scale is based on physical evidence from rock and fossil records that show how Earth has evolved over geologic time. The divisions of the geologic time scale are used to organize events in Earth's history.

1. **Calculate** ✏️ After you read the rest of the lesson, calculate and fill in the duration of each period.

2. **Evaluate Scale** ✏️ Use the time scale to identify the period in which each organism pictured below lived.

3. **SEP Develop Models** ✏️ Draw lines from each fossil or rock pictured on the right to the part of the time scale that represents when it formed.

Precambrian Time / Paleozoic Era

Period	Precambrian Time	Cambrian	Ordovician	Silurian	Devonian	Carboniferous
Began (Millions of Years Ago)	4,600	541	485	444	419	359
Duration (Millions of Years)	4,059		41	25	60	

Organism: *Velociraptor*
Age: about 80 million years
Period: ....

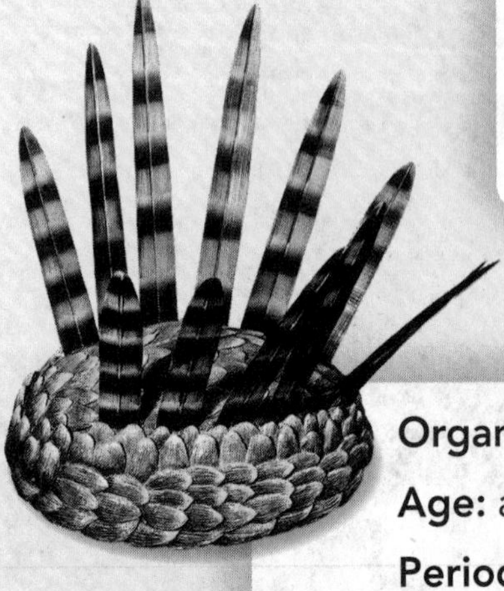

Organism: *Wiwaxia*
Age: about 500 million years
Period: ....

▶ Limestone and shale containing fossil coral from Kentucky and Indiana provide evidence that a shallow sea covered much of North America during the Silurian period.

▼ Geologic evidence such as these deposits from an ancient glacial lake in Washington suggest that a period of major global cooling began about 2.6 million years ago.

◀ Fossilized cyanobacteria that date to about 3.5 billion years ago provide evidence that single-celled organisms actually appeared during the Precambrian.

Mesozoic Era

Cenozoic Era

	Permian		Triassic	Jurassic	Cretaceous		Paleogene	Neogene	Quarternary
	299		252	201	145		66	23	2.6
				56	79			20.4	2.6

Organism: *Smilodon*

Age: between about 2.5 million and 10,000 years

Period: ....

Microscopic Fossil Evidence

Figure 3 This image, produced by a scanning electron microscope, shows the microscopic shells of fossil foraminifera. Information recorded in the shells of these ancient single-celled ocean organisms provides evidence with which scientists track past changes in Earth's climate and refine the geologic time scale.

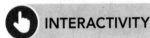

INTERACTIVITY

Review how geologists learn about Earth's history.

HANDS-ON LAB

Investigate Model the geologic time scale.

Dividing Geologic Time

As geologists studied the rock and fossil records, they found major changes in life forms at certain times. Fossils are widely distributed in Earth's rocks. They occur in rocks in a definite order, with new species appearing and old species disappearing. In this way, fossils provided evidence of change on Earth. Geologists used these changes to help identify major events in Earth's history and mark where one unit of geologic time ends and the next begins. Therefore, most divisions of the geologic time scale depend on events in the history of life on Earth. **Figure 2** shows the major divisions of the geologic time scale.

Precambrian Time Geologic time begins with a long span of time called Precambrian (pree KAM bree un) time. Precambrian time covers about 88 percent of Earth's history, from 4.6 billion years ago to 541 million years ago. Few fossils survive from this time period.

Eras Geologists divide the time between the Precambrian and the present into three long units of time called **eras**. During the Paleozoic era, life increased in complexity, and the huge continent Pangaea formed. During the Mesozoic era, dinosaurs became dominant, and Pangaea broke apart. During the Cenozoic era, mammals evolved to become the dominant land animals and the continents moved to their present-day positions.

☑ CHECK POINT Write Informative Texts Provide an example of a defining event for a geologic time division.

....

....

....

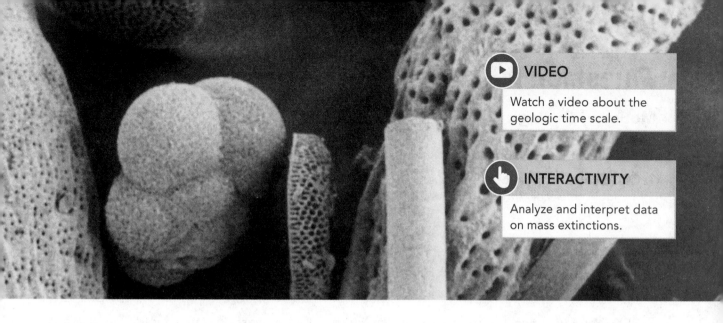

VIDEO

Watch a video about the geologic time scale.

INTERACTIVITY

Analyze and interpret data on mass extinctions.

Periods Eras are subdivided into units of geologic time called **periods**. You can see in **Figure 2** that the Mesozoic era includes three periods: the Triassic period, the Jurassic period, and the Cretaceous period. Each period is defined by certain events. For example, at the end of the Cretaceous period, major volcanic eruptions coincided with the impact on Earth of a huge asteroid. These events significantly changed the global environment.

Refining Earth's History

Our understanding of Earth's history changes with each newly-discovered fossil (**Figure 3**) or rock. Our understanding also changes as the technology used to analyze rocks and fossils advances. That's why geologists continually **refine** the geologic time scale. For example, geologists use the start of a period of major global cooling to mark the beginning of the Quaternary period. Recently, evidence from ocean floor sediments and other sources led scientists to move that boundary from 1.8 to 2.6 million years ago. The new boundary, based on new physical evidence, more accurately reflects a major change in Earth's climate.

Academic Vocabulary
Describe how you might refine something you make or do.

....

....

....

....

Literacy Connection
Write Informative Texts
After you read this page, explain in your own words why Scientists constantly refine the geologic time scale.

....

....

....

....

....

....

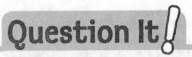

Question It!

Modeling Geologic Time

Suppose your friend makes his own model of the geologic time scale. He decided to use a scale of 1 m = 1 million years. Would your friend's model work?

1. **CCC Scale, Proportion, and Quantity** How would your friend's model differ from the geologic time scale shown in **Figure 2**?

   ....

   ....

   ....

   ....

2. **SEP Cite Evidence** Choose a period from **Figure 2**. Using the scale from your friend's model, determine how much distance that period would cover.

   ....

   ....

   ....

   ....

3. **SEP Develop Models** What would be one advantage and one disadvantage of your friend's model?

   ....

   ....

   ....

   ....

   ....

   ....

☑LESSON 2 Check

 MS-ESS1-4

1. Summarize What is the geologic time scale?

....

....

....

....

....

....

Use Figure 2 in the lesson to help you answer Question 2.

2. CCC Scale, Proportion, and Quantity How is the geologic time scale divided?

....

....

....

....

....

....

....

3. CCC Stability and Change Explain why you think the geologic time scale will or will not change over the next 20 years.

....

....

....

....

....

....

....

....

4. SEP Construct Explanations Give an example of physical evidence used to organize Earth's history on the geologic time scale.

....

....

....

....

....

....

Quest CHECK-IN

In this lesson, you learned about the purpose of the geologic time scale and how the segments of the geologic time scale are defined.

SEP Evaluate Evidence How could you organize the fossils of potential dig sites using the geologic time scale?

....

....

....

....

....

👆 INTERACTIVITY

A Matter of Time

Go online to learn about fossils found at each potential dig site and plot them on the geologic time scale.

LESSON 3 Major Events in Earth's History

HANDS-ON LAB

uInvestigate Analyze changes in biodiversity over time.

MS-ESS1-4 Construct a scientific explanation based on evidence from rock strata for how the geologic time scale is used to organize Earth's 4.6-billion-year-old history.

Connect It!

✏️ **Circle any organisms you recognize in this Carboniferous swamp.**

Determine Similarities How was life during the Carboniferous period similar to life today?

....

....

Make Observations What do you think conditions were like during the Carboniferous period in this dragonfly's habitat?

....

....

....

Major Events in the Paleozoic Era

HANDS-ON LAB

и**Investigate** Analyze changes in biodiversity over time.

Earth has a long history of change, starting 4.6 billion years ago when the planet formed. The geologic time scale, interpreted from the rock and fossil records, provides a way to organize that long history of change. The development and evolution of organisms is just one example of the changes that have taken place. For example, **Figure 1** shows how different life was on Earth 300 million years ago.

Through most of Earth's history, during Precambrian time, the only living things were single-celled organisms. Near the end of the Precambrian, more complex living things evolved. Feathery, plantlike organisms anchored themselves to the seafloor. Jellyfish-like organisms floated in the oceans. Then, a much greater variety of living things evolved during the next phase of geologic time—the Paleozoic era.

The Cambrian Explosion During the first part of the Paleozoic era, known as the Cambrian period, life took a big leap forward. Many different kinds of organisms evolved, including some that had hard parts such as shells and outer skeletons. This evolutionary event is called the Cambrian explosion because so many new life forms appeared within a relatively short time. To date these changes, scientists use the law of superposition and other methods to find relative ages and radioactive dating to find absolute ages in the geologic record.

At this time, all animals lived in the sea. Many were animals without backbones, or **invertebrates**. Common invertebrates included jellyfish, worms, sponges, clam-like brachiopods, and trilobites.

Ancient Swamp Life
Figure 1 This artist's drawing shows life in a swampy forest during the Carboniferous period, which occurred about 200 million years after the Cambrian period.

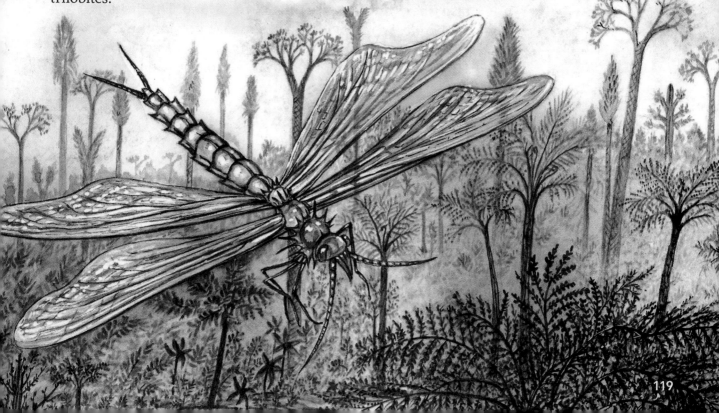

Early Organisms

Figure 2 ✎ These fossils provide evidence of the evolution of organisms during the Paleozoic era. Write the period during which the organism appeared in the fossil record.

Jawless Fish ....

First Vertebrates and Land Plants The Ordovician period is the second segment of the Paleozoic era. The first vertebrates, including jawless fish, evolved during the Ordovician. A **vertebrate** is an animal with a backbone. The first insects may have evolved at this time, along with land plants.

Plants grew abundantly during the next period, the Silurian. These simple plants grew low to the ground in damp areas. By the Devonian period that followed, plants evolved that could grow in drier areas. Among these plants were the earliest ferns.

Both invertebrates and vertebrates lived in the Devonian seas. Even though the invertebrates were more numerous, the Devonian is often called the Age of Fish. Every main group of fish, including sharks, was present in the oceans. Most fish had jaws, bony skeletons, and scales on their bodies.

Animals Reach Land The Devonian period was also when vertebrates began to live on land. The first land vertebrates were lungfish with strong, muscular fins. The first amphibians evolved from these lungfish. An **amphibian** (am FIB ee un) is an animal that lives part of its life on land and part of its life in water.

Animals and Plants Evolve Further The Carboniferous period followed the Devonian in the late Paleozoic era. During this period, the amniote egg (an egg filled with special fluids) evolved. This important adaptation allowed animals to lay eggs on land without the eggs drying out. This adaptation coincides with the appearance of reptiles in the fossil record. **Reptiles** have scaly skin and lay eggs that have tough, leathery shells.

During the Carboniferous, winged insects evolved into many new forms, including huge dragonflies and cockroaches. Giant ferns, mosses, and cone-bearing plants formed vast swampy forests. These plants resembled plants that live in tropical and temperate areas today.

Literacy Connection

Cite Textual Evidence Underline the evidence that supports the statement "Animals and plants evolved further during the Carboniferous Period."

Pangaea Over the course of the Paleozoic era, Earth's continents slowly moved together to form a great landmass, or supercontinent, called Pangaea (pan JEE uh). The formation of Pangaea caused deserts to expand in the tropics and sheets of ice to cover land closer to the South Pole.

Mass Extinction The organisms in **Figure 2** represent the huge diversity of life that evolved during the Paleozoic era. However, during the Permian period at the end of the Paleozoic, a major change occurred and most species of life on Earth died out during the worst extinction event in Earth's history. This was a **mass extinction**, an event during which many types of living things became extinct at the same time. Scientists estimate that about 90 percent of all ocean species and 70 percent of species on land died out. Even widespread organisms such as trilobites became extinct.

Scientists aren't sure what caused this extinction. Some scientists think multiple volcanoes erupted so much dust and debris that the energy from the sun was blocked. This would have prevented plants from performing photosynthesis. Other scientists think a rise in global temperatures was to blame. Scientists have also found that the amount of carbon dioxide in the oceans increased and the amount of oxygen declined. It would have been difficult for organisms to quickly adjust to these changes. All of these **factors** likely contributed to the mass extinction.

☑ CHECK POINT **Cite Textual Evidence** According to the text, what impact did the amniote egg have on life forms on Earth?

....

....

....

....

INTERACTIVITY

Observe fossils to make deductions about the organisms and their environments.

Academic Vocabulary

What two factors determined what you did over the weekend?

....

....

....

....

....

....

Mesozoic Winged Animals

Figure 3 The illustration below shows an artist's idea of what a *Dimorphodon* (a type of pterosaur) and an *Archaeopteryx* looked like.

1. Claim Did these winged animals evolve from a recent common ancestor?

....

2. Evidence List the evidence that supports your claim

....
....
....
....
....

3. Reasoning Explain how your evidence supports your claim.

....
....
....
....
....
....

Major Events in the Mesozoic Era

Mass extinctions are followed by increases in evolution and variation. The mass extinction at the end of the Paleozoic era became an opportunity for many new life forms, including dinosaurs, to develop in the Mesozoic era.

Age of Reptiles

Some living things managed to survive the Permian mass extinction. Plants and animals that survived included fish, insects, reptiles, and cone-bearing plants called conifers. Reptiles were so successful during the Mesozoic era that this time is often called the Age of Reptiles. The first dinosaurs appeared during the first period of the Mesozoic era, called the Triassic period.

First Mammals

Mammals also first appeared during the Triassic period. A **mammal** is a vertebrate that controls its own body temperature and feeds milk to its young. Mammals in the Triassic period were very small—about the size of a mouse.

Reptiles and Birds

During the Jurassic period, the second segment of the Mesozoic era, dinosaurs were the dominant land animals. Scientists have identified several hundred different kinds of dinosaurs, including some that ate plants and some that were predators. One plant-eating dinosaur, *Brachiosaurus*, was 26 meters long!

The ocean and seas during this period were also filled with diverse life forms, including sharks, rays, giant marine crocodiles, and plesiosaurs. Plesiosaurs had long necks and paddle-like fins.

Late in the Jurassic, dinosaurs with some characteristics of birds appeared in the skies. Birds and *Archaeopteryx,* which means "ancient winged one," evolved from dinosaurs. The sky also had flying reptiles, called pterosaurs, and many varieties of insects. Use **Figure 3** to compare *Archaeopteryx* and a type of pterosaur called *Dimorphodon*.

Dimorphodon

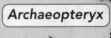
Archaeopteryx

Flowering Plants The Cretaceous period is the final and longest segment of the Mesozoic era. Reptiles, including dinosaurs, were still widespread throughout the Cretaceous. Ancient birds evolved better adaptations for flying and began to replace flying reptiles.

One of the most important events of the Cretaceous period was the evolution of flowering plants, or angiosperms. Unlike conifers, flowering plants produce seeds that are inside a fruit. Many flowering plants you may recognize today first appeared during this time, such as magnolias, figs, and willows.

Another Mass Extinction
At the end of the Cretaceous, another mass extinction occurred. Scientists **hypothesize** that this mass extinction occurred when an asteroid struck Earth at a time when extreme volcanic activity in the area that is now India had weakened environments. This mass extinction wiped out more than half of all plant and animal groups, including the dinosaurs. Use **Figure 4** to illustrate the event.

✓ CHECK POINT **Use Information** How did organisms from the Mesozoic era differ from organisms of the Paleozoic?

....

....

....

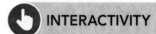
INTERACTIVITY

Examine evidence that shows major changes over time.

Reflect Which major event or time in Earth's history would you most like to witness? In your science notebook, describe the event or time period you would like to experience. Explain how you could gather evidence to help evaluate explanations of Earth's history.

Academic Vocabulary
Use *hypothesize* in a sentence about a subject other than science.

....

....

....

Model It

The End of the Dinosaurs
Figure 4 In 1980, University of California geologist Walter Alvarez and his father, physicist Luis Alvarez, found evidence that an asteroid hit Earth more than 60 million years ago. The crater it formed was later found near present-day southeastern Mexico. Show how this event, combined with the environment at the time, contributed to the mass extinction.

SEP Develop Models 🖉
Complete the comic strip.
Draw events that led to the extinction of the dinosaurs. Label each stage.
Add a title.

Title: ....

Math Toolbox
Comparing Mammal Height

Many giant mammals evolved in the Cenozoic era. Geologists have unearthed several large mammals at the La Brea tar pits in Los Angeles, California, including the *Megatherium*. This giant sloth is related to the modern sloth but is much taller.

1. **Measure** Use the ruler to measure the height of each sloth.

   Megatherium height: about ....

   Modern sloth height: about ....

2. **Represent Quantitative Relationships** About how many times taller was *Megatherium* than a modern sloth? Complete the equation below, in which *m* is the height of *Megatherium* and *s* is the height of the modern sloth.

   $m = s \times$ ....

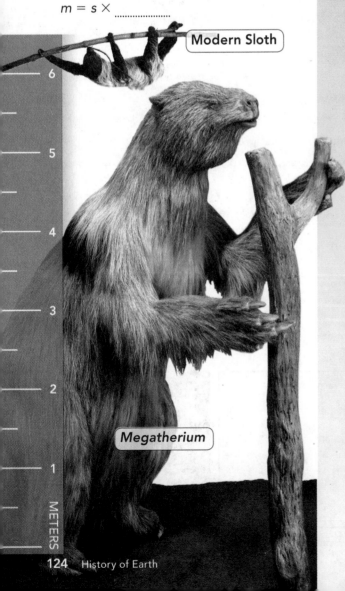

Modern Sloth

Megatherium

6

5

4

3

2

1

METERS

Major Events in the Cenozoic Era

During the Mesozoic era, small mammals had to compete with dinosaurs and other animals for food and places to live. The mass extinction at the end of that era created an opportunity for the species that did survive, including some mammals. During the Cenozoic era that followed, mammals evolved to live in many different environments—on land, in water, and even in the air. Geologists have found evidence for the spread of mammals in the fossils, rocks, and sediment of the early Cenozoic era.

Mammals Thrive The Cenozoic begins with the Paleogene and Neogene periods. During these periods, Earth's climate became gradually cooler over time. As the continents drifted apart, ocean basins widened and mammals such as whales and dolphins evolved. On land, mammals flourished. Some birds and mammals became very large. For instance, the great saber-toothed cat, *Smilodon,* was nearly one and a half times as heavy as a modern lion. (You saw the saber-toothed cat, which is the state fossil of California, in Lesson 2.) Forests thinned, making space for flowering plants and grasses to become more dominant.

Ice Ages At the start of the Quaternary period, large sheets of ice began to appear on Earth's surface. Earth's climate continued to cool and warm in cycles, causing a series of ice ages followed by warmer periods. During the last ice age, about 30 percent of Earth's surface was covered in thick glaciers. The latest warm period began between 10,000 and 20,000 years ago. During that time, sea levels rose and most of the glaciers melted.

Humans The Quaternary period is sometimes referred to as the "Age of Humans." *Homo erectus,* an ancestor of modern humans, appears in the fossil record near the start of the period, while modern humans appeared about 190,000 years ago. By about 12,000 to 15,000 years ago, humans had migrated to every continent except Antarctica.

How Scientists Organize Earth's History

Figure 5 🖉 This timeline shows major events in Earth's history. It is a model that you can use to study events that occur over geologic time. (Note that, to make the timeline easier to read, periods are not drawn to scale.) Circle the periods during which mass extinctions occurred.

▶ VIDEO

Watch a video about major events in Earth's history.

Events	Period	Began (Millions of Years Ago)	
Earth forms. First single-celled and multi-celled organisms evolve.		4,600	PRECAMBRIAN TIME
"Explosion" of new forms of life occurs. Invertebrates such as trilobites are common. 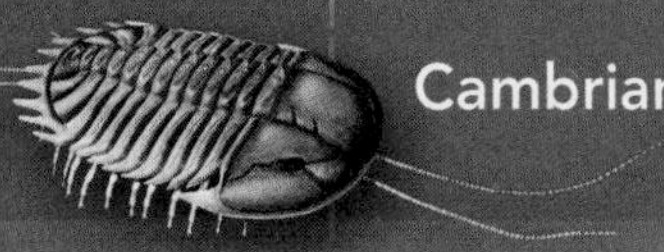	Cambrian	541	PALEOZOIC ERA
First vertebrates, insects, and land plants evolve.	Ordovician	485	
Early fish are common in seas.	Silurian	444	
"Age of Fish" occurs, with many different kinds of fish. Lungfish and amphibians first reach land.	Devonian	419	
Appalachian Mountains form. Reptiles and giant insects evolve. Ferns and cone-bearing plants form forests.	Carboniferous	359	
Pangaea forms. Mass extinction kills most species.	Permian	299	
Reptiles flourish, including the first dinosaurs. First mammals evolve. 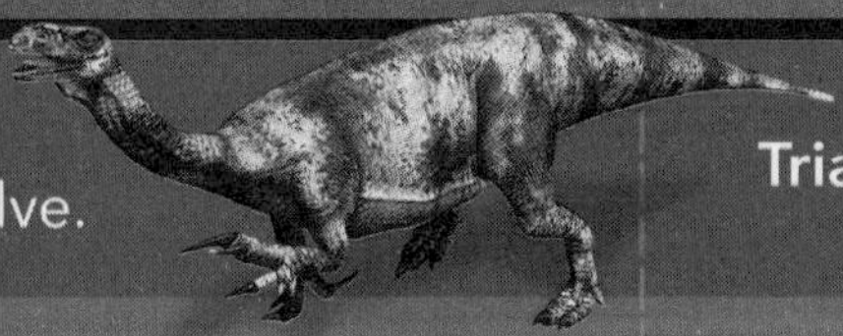	Triassic	252	MESOZOIC ERA
Dinosaurs become common. First birds evolve.	Jurassic	201	
Dinosaurs are widespread. Birds begin to replace flying reptiles. Flowering plants appear. Mass extinction occurs.	Cretaceous	145	
Mammals flourish. Grasses first spread widely.	Paleogene	66	CENOZOIC ERA
The Andes and Himalayas form. Some mammals and birds become very large.	Neogene	23	
Ice ages occur. Many kinds of animals thrive. First modern humans evolve. 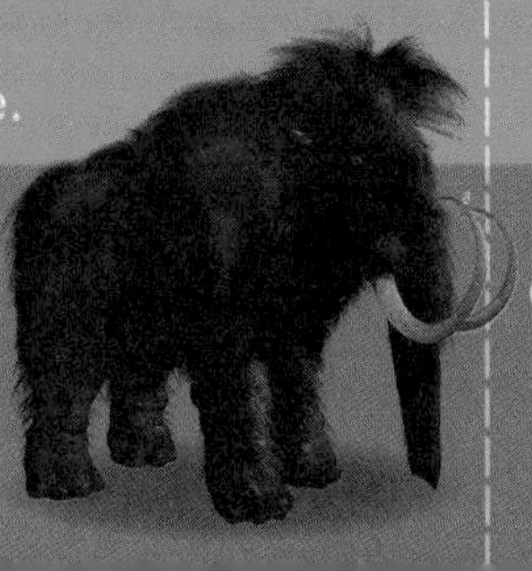	Quarternary	2.6	

MS-ESS1-4

1. Sequence Arrange the following organisms in order from earliest to latest appearance: amphibians, jawless fish, trilobites, bony fish.

....
....
....
....

2. Synthesize Information Why do you think scientists use mass extinctions to separate one era from another?

....
....
....
....
....
....
....
....
....
....
....
....

3. SEP Cite Evidence Identify a major event in Earth's past and describe the supporting evidence for that event you would expect to observe in the fossil record.

....
....
....
....
....
....
....
....
....
....
....

Quest CHECK-IN

In this lesson, you learned about major events that help to define and organize Earth's history.

Evaluate Reasoning How can knowing about Earth's history help you to choose your dig site?

....
....
....
....
....

👆 INTERACTIVITY

Time to Choose the Dig Site

Go online to conduct research about *Dimetrodon* to make the final site selection.

MS-ESS1-4, EP&CIIc, EP&CVa

A New Mass Extinction?

When a species dies out, we say it is *extinct*. When large numbers of species die out at the same time, scientists use the term *mass extinction*. Scientists know of multiple mass extinctions in Earth's history. Some suggest that another mass extinction is approaching.

One factor that can lead to extinctions is the introduction of plant and animal species into new environments. Some of this is due to species migration. Animals and plants can move into new areas where temperature and climate patterns have become more favorable due to global warming. However, most species are brought to new areas by humans. In many cases, this leads to the disappearance of native species.

Habitat loss is another factor that leads to extinctions. When habitats are lost, the species that live within them no longer have the space or resources to live. As human communities expand, so does the human need for resources, such as fuel, land, and food. Habitats are cleared or changed to meet those needs, and the organisms that lived there may die off. For example, destruction of wetlands in the Sacramento valley, located in California's Central Valley, threatens migrating shore birds.

Climate change caused by global warming may also lead to extinctions. Our increased use of fossil fuels and the accompanying rise in carbon dioxide in the atmosphere has led to a steady increase in global temperatures. As temperatures rise, environments change. Species that cannot adapt to the changes may die out.

Most scientists agree that there is a real threat of another mass extinction. However, there are still steps people can take to prevent or minimize the loss of our biodiversity.

Urban development to accommodate a growing human population leads to habitat loss.

MY COMMUNITY

What steps can you take in your community to change our path away from mass extinction? What can you do to influence lawmakers? Use the library and the Internet to find facts and evidence that will support your ideas.

Evidence-Based Assessment

A team of geologists explores an area of land that was once an ancient sea. They dig for fossils of marine organisms at three locations. The geologists collect and record information about the fossils they have discovered and the rock layers that the fossils were found in. The data are summarized in the diagram.

The geologists attempt to identify an index fossil to help them analyze the relative ages of the rock layers and to determine how the layers at the three sites correspond to one another. The researchers attempt to determine the relative ages of the layers and the fossils of marine organisms they have dug up.

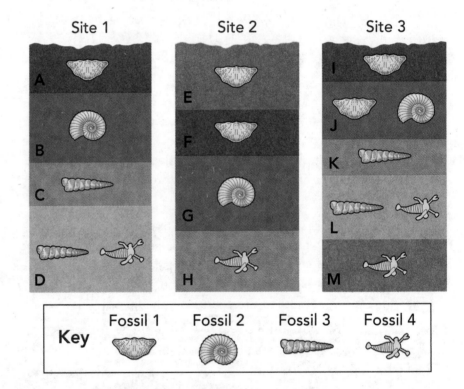

1. **SEP Interpret Data** Which is an index fossil?
   A. Fossil 1
   B. Fossil 2
   C. Fossil 3
   D. Fossil 4

2. **Evaluate Quantity** Which statements about the relative ages of the rock layers is true? Select all that apply.
   ☐ Layers B, G, and J are the same age.
   ☐ Layer E is the youngest layer.
   ☐ Layers D, H, and J are the same age.
   ☐ Layers H and M are the oldest layers.
   ☐ Layer A is the youngest layer.
   ☐ Layers D and H are the oldest layers.

3. **Apply Scientific Reasoning** Based on the data, complete the sentence below to draw conclusions about the relative ages of Fossils 1 and 2. Circle all options that apply.

   Fossil 1 is (older than / younger than / the same age as) Fossil 2. This is true because, according to the law of superposition, (younger / older) rock is found on top of (younger / older) rock.

4. **SEP Engage in Argument** A peer claims that Fossil 2 is older than Fossil 3. Using evidence from the rock layers, explain why the evidence does not support their claim.

   ....
   ....
   ....
   ....
   ....
   ....
   ....
   ....
   ....
   ....
   ....

5. **SEP Construct Explanations** Fossil 2 is about 300 million years old. Testing reveals that Layer M is about 400 million years old. The geologists conclude that Fossil 3 is an organism that likely lived about 350 million years ago. Do you agree? Support your answer using evidence from the diagram.

   ....
   ....
   ....
   ....
   ....
   ....
   ....

Quest FINDINGS

Complete the Quest!

Present your choice of dig site in a report to the head of the science museum that is sponsoring the _Dimetrodon_ exhibit. In your report, include evidence and scientific reasoning that support your choice.

Evaluate Your Plan What roles did the rock and fossil record play in determining your choice of dig site?

....
....
....
....
....

👆 **INTERACTIVITY**

Reflect on the Big Fossil Hunt

MS-ESS1-4

Core Sampling Through Time

How can you **determine** the **relative ages of rock layers** in different locations?

Materials

(per group)

- four models positioned around the classroom representing rock layers
- plastic gloves
- metric ruler
- large-diameter drinking straw
- long dowel or rod that fits into the straw
- several sheets of paper
- colored pencils

Safety

Be sure to follow all safety guidelines provided by your teacher. The Safety Appendix of your textbook provides more details about the safety icons.

Background

Phenomenon Visitors to a local state park see a variety of rocks and fossils on the surface in different locations. They often ask, Are the rocks here the same age as those over there? In your role as volunteer park ranger, how will you answer? You will need to find out how the ages of the rocks throughout the park compare.

You know that you can learn about the order of events in Earth's history by studying rocks. However, geologists cannot simply flip through layers of sedimentary rock like the pages in a magazine to study them. Instead, they must analyze samples taken from deep below the surface. In a process called *coring*, hollow tubes are driven into sedimentary rock layers. When the tubes are pulled out, they contain samples of all the layers.

In this activity, you will illustrate the geologic history of the park using the data you gather through core sampling.

Plan Your Investigation

HANDS-ON LAB

Demonstrate Go online for a downloadable worksheet of this lab.

- [ ] 1. Your teacher positioned four models around the classroom. The models represent sedimentary rock layers, some with index fossils, in different locations throughout the park.

- [ ] 2. **Student Discourse** Design an investigation to discover the geologic history of the park by drilling and analyzing core samples. Discuss the following questions, with your team members, as you form your plan:

    - In which locations should you drill to get a complete picture of the rocks throughout the park so you can compare their ages?

    - How many core samples will you drill in each location?

    - How will you record what you observe in the core samples?

    - How will you compare the locations of sediment layers and index fossils?

    - How will you present your findings?

- [ ] 2. Use the space provided to summarize your investigation. Show your plan to your teacher for approval.

- [ ] 3. Conduct your investigation, record your observations, and report your findings according to your plan.

Procedure

....
....
....
....
....
....
....
....
....
....
....
....
....

Evidence Gathered from Core Samples

Analyze and Interpret Data

1. **SEP Develop Models** Use your observations and analysis to make a diagram of the complete geologic history of the park.

2. **SEP Use Models** Compare the geologic record at the different locations represented by your model core samples. Explain any differences you observe.

   ....

   ....

3. **CCC Patterns** Which rock layers at the different locations do you think are the same age? Explain your answer using evidence.

   ....

   ....

4. **Apply Scientific Reasoning** Choose two core samples that represent different locations in the park. Compare the ages of the rocks on the surface. Explain how you determined their relative ages.

   ....

   ....

   ....

   ....

   ....

Could DINOSAURS Roar?

Vegavis is not the direct ancestor of modern-day ducks or chickens, but it is closely related to waterfowl such as geese.

So many movies have dinosaurs roaring as they roam across the landscape shredding trees and devouring prey the size of SUVs. Fossil evidence, however, supports a more silent world. In fact, it wasn't until about 65 to 68 million years ago that a very important piece of anatomy developed—the syrinx. Think of it as a voice box.

In 1992, on an Antarctic island, scientists found a fossil of *Vegavis iaai*, a bird that lived between 68 and 65 million years ago. At that time in Earth's history, Antarctica had a tropical climate. It wasn't until recently that technology revealed the most important find in the fossil: a syrinx.

Connections to Modern-Day Birds

The presence of a syrinx helps us to understand the ancestry of modern birds. Because of the asymmetrical structure of the syrinx, scientists speculate that the bird may have honked like a goose. Scientists analyzed the same structures in 12 living birds and compared them to the next oldest fossilized syrinx that was available. They found similarities in structure across the samples. Their findings supported the claim that *Vegavis iaai* was related to modern birds, but not an ancestor of modern reptiles, who are also able to vocalize through the larynx.

It would take a large brain to produce a selection of noises that meant something. If dinosaurs were able to vocalize or utter any sounds at all, then the sounds they made would have been a far cry from what you hear in the movies.

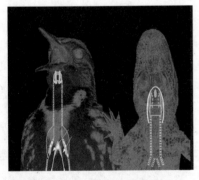

Location of syrinx in living songbird compared to larynx in an alligator

The presence of a syrinx in the *Vegavis iaai* fossil strongly suggests that the bird was capable of producing sounds. In the songbird, as in *Vegavis*, the syrinx is located in the chest. In the alligator, the larynx is located in the throat.

Photo Credit: Dr. Julia Clarke, University of Texas at Austin

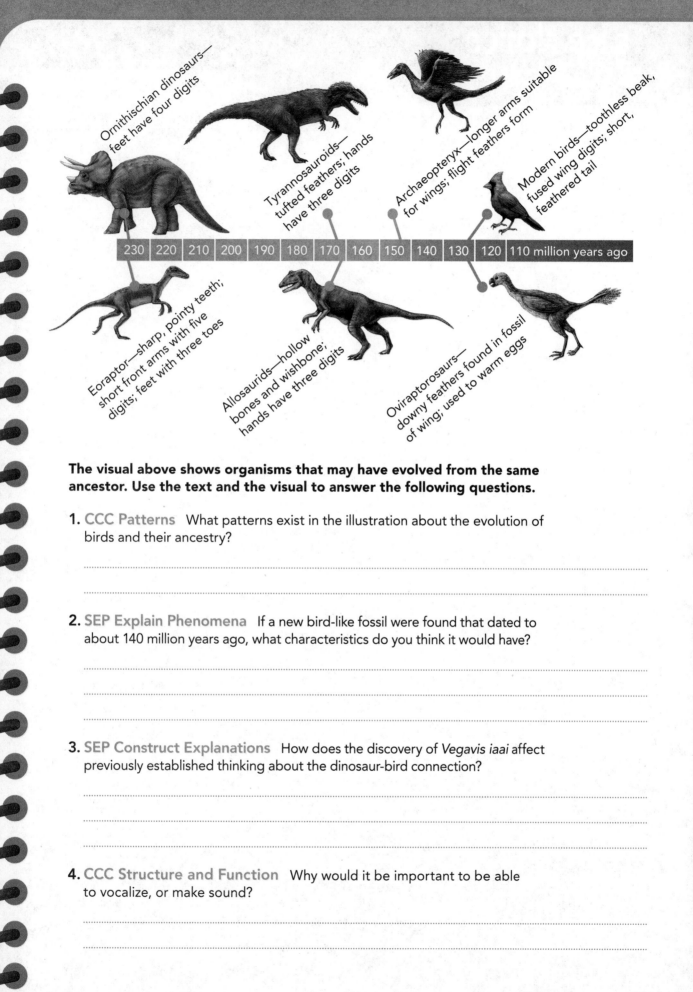

Ornithischian dinosaurs— feet have four digits

Tyrannosauroids— tufted feathers; hands have three digits

Archaeopteryx—longer arms suitable for wings; flight feathers form

Modern birds—toothless beak, fused wing digits; short, feathered tail

| 230 | 220 | 210 | 200 | 190 | 180 | 170 | 160 | 150 | 140 | 130 | 120 | 110 million years ago |

Eoraptor—sharp, pointy teeth; short front arms with five digits; feet with three toes

Allosaurids—hollow bones and wishbone; hands have three digits

Oviraptorosaurs— downy feathers found in fossil of wing; used to warm eggs

The visual above shows organisms that may have evolved from the same ancestor. Use the text and the visual to answer the following questions.

1. CCC Patterns What patterns exist in the illustration about the evolution of birds and their ancestry?

....

....

2. SEP Explain Phenomena If a new bird-like fossil were found that dated to about 140 million years ago, what characteristics do you think it would have?

....

....

....

3. SEP Construct Explanations How does the discovery of *Vegavis iaai* affect previously established thinking about the dinosaur-bird connection?

....

....

....

4. CCC Structure and Function Why would it be important to be able to vocalize, or make sound?

....

....

Take Notes

Use this space for recording notes and sketching out ideas.

Evidence **Now that you have completed all three topics within this segment, do the following task.**

Impacts on Evolution in California

Case Study Now that you have learned about the evidence that helps scientists to explain how changes in Earth's system processes and human activities can bring about changes in life forms, you can take a closer look at what drives change in a particular species. Consider the impact of climate change due to human activities and how global warming could alter various ecosystems in California. Identify a specific species for your research. It must be a species found in California or along its coasts. The species could be a plant, mammal, bird, reptile, amphibian, or fish. The species may live in California or migrate through it.

Research your chosen species to learn more about it. Find out how long it has inhabited a California ecosystem and if it appears in the fossil record. Determine how your species has changed over time, if at all. Consider what factors might have caused the organism to change. List ways in which your chosen species could adapt to an extreme climate event. What sort of traits would have to be passed from parent to offspring? Also list any steps that could be taken now to protect it from the effects of climate change.

Describe any instance where human activities, either directly or indirectly, might be causing rapid environmental change. Explain how your species could adapt to that change and what might happen if it cannot adapt.

Extreme climate change in California could impact both of these species.

Bull Trout

American Pika

Communicate a Solution

Based on your research, answer the following questions.

1. **SEP Communicate Information** Describe the species you researched, its habitat in California, and how climate change is affecting it. Also explain how human activities have directly or indirectly impacted the species.

....

....

....

....

....

....

....

....

....

....

....

2. **SEP Construct Explanations** If the species you researched goes extinct, how would the species be reflected in the fossil record? Would the species be fossilized? Explain.

....

....

....

....

3. **Explain Phenomena** How could an extreme climate change, such as global warming, affect the evolution of the species you researched? Explain.

....

....

....

....

....

4. CCC Stability and Change Natural selection is a process that occurs slowly over time. What sort of adaptations would need to be present in the organism's population in order for it to survive environmental changes, such as the effects of climate change? Can these adaptations be passed from one generation to the next? How does this relate to evolution?

5. Connect to the Environment What can humans do to protect your species? Present one way to protect the species with a solution that could be easily implemented.

6. CCC Cause and Effect Earlier in this segment, you drew a conclusion about the impact of extreme climate change on leatherback sea turtles in California. Consider what you learned researching your species. How might the human impact of climate change affect the two different species?

Safety Symbols

These symbols warn of possible dangers in the laboratory and remind you to work carefully.

 Safety Goggles Wear safety goggles to protect your eyes in any activity involving chemicals, flames or heating, or glassware.

 Lab Apron Wear a laboratory apron to protect your skin and clothing from damage.

 Breakage Handle breakable materials, such as glassware, with care. Do not touch broken glassware.

 Heat-Resistant Gloves Use an oven mitt or other hand protection when handling hot materials, such as hot plates or hot glassware.

 Plastic Gloves Wear disposable plastic gloves when working with harmful chemicals and organisms. Keep your hands away from your face, and dispose of the gloves according to your teacher's instructions.

 Heating Use a clamp or tongs to pick up hot glassware. Do not touch hot objects with your bare hands.

 Flames Before you work with flames, tie back loose hair and clothing. Follow your teacher's instructions about lighting and extinguishing flames.

 No Flames When using flammable materials, make sure there are no flames, sparks, or other exposed heat sources present.

 Corrosive Chemical Avoid getting acid or other corrosive chemicals on your skin or clothing or in your eyes. Do not inhale the vapors. Wash your hands after the activity.

 Poison Do not let any poisonous chemical come into contact with your skin, and do not inhale its vapors. Wash your hands when you are finished with the activity.

 Fumes Work in a well-ventilated area when harmful vapors may be involved. Avoid inhaling vapors directly. Test an odor only when directed to do so by your teacher, and use a wafting motion to direct the vapor toward your nose.

 Sharp Object Scissors, scalpels, knives, needles, pins, and tacks can cut your skin. Always direct a sharp edge or point away from yourself and others.

 Animal Safety Treat live or preserved animals or animal parts with care to avoid harming the animals or yourself. Wash your hands when you are finished with the activity.

 Plant Safety Handle plants only as directed by your teacher. If you are allergic to certain plants, tell your teacher; do not do an activity involving those plants. Avoid touching harmful plants such as poison ivy. Wash your hands when you are finished with the activity.

 Electric Shock To avoid electric shock, never use electrical equipment around water, when the equipment is wet, or when your hands are wet. Be sure cords are untangled and cannot trip anyone. Unplug equipment not in use.

 Physical Safety When an experiment involves physical activity, avoid injuring yourself or others. Alert your teacher if there is any reason you should not participate.

 Disposal Dispose of chemicals and other laboratory materials safely. Follow the instructions from your teacher.

 Hand Washing Wash your hands thoroughly when finished with an activity. Use soap and warm water. Rinse well.

 General Safety Awareness When this symbol appears, follow the instructions provided. When you are asked to develop your own procedure in a lab, have your teacher approve your plan.

GLOSSARY

A

absolute age The age of a rock given as the number of years since the rock formed.

absorption The transfer of energy from a wave to a material that it encounters.

acceleration The rate at which velocity changes.

acid rain Rain or another form of precipitation that is more acidic than normal, caused by the release of molecules of sulfur dioxide and nitrogen oxide into the air.

adaptation An inherited behavior or physical characteristic that helps an organism survive and reproduce in its environment.

amphibian A vertebrate whose body temperature is determined by the temperature of its environment, and that lives its early life in water and its adult life on land.

amplitude The height of a transverse wave from the center to a crest or trough.

analog signal A signal that allows for a continuous record of some kind of action.

artificial selection The process by which humans breed only those organisms with desired traits to produce the next generation; selective breeding.

asteroid One of the rocky objects revolving around the sun that is too small and numerous to be considered a planet.

astronomical unit A unit of distance equal to the average distance between Earth and the sun, about 150 million kilometers.

autosomal chromosomes The 22 pairs of chromosomes that are not sex chromosomes.

axis An imaginary line that passes through a planet's center and its north and south poles, about which the planet rotates.

B

bandwidth The amount of information that can be transmitted in bits per second.

birth rate The number of people born per 1,000 individuals for a certain period of time.

C

chromosome A threadlike structure within a cell's nucleus that contains DNA that is passed from one generation to the next.

clone An organism that is genetically identical to the organism from which it was produced.

comet A loose collection of ice and dust that orbits the sun, typically in a long, narrow orbit.

competition The struggle between organisms to survive as they attempt to use the same limited resources in the same place at the same time.

concave A mirror with a surface that curves inward or a lens that is thinner at the center than at the edges.

conductor A material that allows electric charges to flow.

conservation The practice of using less of a resource so that it can last longer.

constellation A pattern or grouping of stars that people imagine to represent a figure or object.

convex A mirror that curves outward or lens that is thicker in the center than at the edges.

D

death rate The number of deaths per 1,000 individuals in a certain period of time.

decibel (dB) A unit used to compare the loudness of different sounds.

deforestation The removal of forests to use the land for other reasons.

desertification The advance of desert-like conditions into areas that previously were fertile.

diffraction The bending or spreading of waves as they move around a barrier or pass through an opening.

diffuse reflection Reflection that occurs when parallel light rays hit an uneven surface and all reflect at different angles.

digital signal A signal that allows for a record of numerical values of an action at a set of continuous time intervals.

Doppler effect The change in frequency of a wave as its source moves in relation to an observer.

E

eclipse The partial or total blocking of one object in space by another.

elastic potential energy The energy associated with objects that can be compressed or stretched.

electric current The continuous flow of electrical charges through a material.

electric field The region around a charged object where the object's electric force is exerted on other charged objects.

electric force The force between charged objects.

electric motor A device that transforms electrical energy to mechanical energy.

electromagnet A magnet created by wrapping a coil of wire with a current running through it around a core of material that is easily magnetized.

electromagnetic induction The process of generating an electric current from the motion of a conductor through a magnetic field.

electromagnetic signal Information that is sent as a pattern of electromagnetic waves, such as visible light, microwaves, and radio waves.

electromagnetism The relationship between electricity and magnetism.

electronic signal Information that is sent as a pattern in a controlled flow of current through a circuit.

ellipse An oval shape, which may be elongated or nearly circular; the shape of the planets' orbits.

embryo The young organism that develops from a zygote.

emissions Pollutants that are released into the air.

energy The ability to cause change.

equinox Either of the two days of the year on which neither hemisphere is tilted toward or away from the sun.

era One of the three long units of geologic time between the Precambrian and the present.

erosion The process by which water, ice, wind, or gravity moves weathered particles of rock and soil.

evolution Change over time; the process by which modern organisms have descended from ancient organisms.

exponential growth A rate of change that increases more and more rapidly over time.

extinct Term used to refer to a group of related organisms that has died out and has no living members.

---------------------- F ----------------------

fitness How well an organism can survive and reproduce in its environment.

focal point The point at which light rays parallel to the optical axis meet, after being reflected (or refracted) by a mirror (or lens).

force A push or pull exerted on an object.

fossil The preserved remains or traces of an organism that lived in the past.

fossil record All the fossils that have been discovered and what scientists have learned from them.

frequency The number of complete waves that pass a given point in a certain amount of time.

friction The force that two surfaces exert on each other when they rub against each other.

---------------------- G ----------------------

galaxy A huge group of single stars, star systems, star clusters, dust, and gas bound together by gravity.

galvanometer A device that uses an electromagnet to detect small amounts of current.

gene therapy The process of replacing an absent or faulty gene with a normal working gene to treat a disease or medical disorder.

generator A device that transforms mechanical energy into electrical energy.

genetic engineering The transfer of a gene from the DNA of one organism into another organism, in order to produce an organism with desired traits.

genome The complete set of genetic information that an organism carries in its DNA.

geocentric Term describing a model of the universe in which Earth is at the center of the revolving planets and stars.

geologic time scale A record of the geologic events and life forms in Earth's history.

gravitational potential energy The potential energy related to an object's vertical position.

gravity The attractive force between objects; the force that moves objects downhill.

---------------------- H ----------------------

heliocentric Term describing a model of the solar system in which Earth and the other planets revolve around the sun.

homologous structures Structures that are similar in different species and that have been inherited from a common ancestor.

GLOSSARY

I

inertia The tendency of an object to resist a change in motion.

information technology Computer and telecommunication hardware and software that store, transmit, receive, and manipulate information.

intensity The amount of energy per second carried through a unit area by a wave.

interference The interaction between waves that meet.

invertebrate An animal without a backbone.

K

kinetic energy Energy that an object possesses by virtue of being in motion.

L

law of conservation of energy The law that states that energy is conserved. When one object loses energy, other objects must gain it.

law of superposition The geologic principle that states that in horizontal layers of sedimentary rock, each layer is older than the layer above it and younger than the layer below it.

law of universal gravitation The scientific law that states that every object in the universe attracts every other object.

longitudinal wave A wave that moves the medium in a direction parallel to the direction in which the wave travels.

loudness The perception of the energy of a sound.

M

magnet Any material that attracts iron and materials that contain iron.

magnetic field The region around a magnet where the magnetic force is exerted.

magnetic force A force produced when magnetic poles interact.

magnetic pole The ends of a magnetic object, where the magnetic force is strongest.

magnetism The force of attraction or repulsion of magnetic materials.

mammal A vertebrate whose body temperature is regulated by its internal heat, and that has skin covered with hair or fur and glands that produce milk to feed its young.

mass extinction When many types of living things become extinct at the same time.

mechanical wave A wave that requires a medium through which to travel.

mechanism The natural process by which something takes place.

medium The material through which a wave travels.

meteor A streak of light in the sky produced by the burning of a meteoroid in Earth's atmosphere.

meteoroid A chunk of rock or dust in space, generally smaller than an asteroid.

moon A natural satellite that orbits a planet.

motion The state in which one object's distance from another is changing.

mutation Any change in the DNA of a gene or a chromosome.

N

natural resource Anything naturally occurring in the environment that humans use.

natural selection The process by which organisms that are best adapted to their environment are most likely to survive and reproduce.

net force The overall force on an object when all the individual forces acting on it are added together.

newton A unit of measure that equals the force required to accelerate 1 kilogram of mass at 1 meter per second per second.

noise Random signals from the environment that can alter the output of a signal.

nonpoint source A widely spread source of pollution that is difficult to link to a specific point of origin.

nonrenewable resource A natural resource that is not replaced in a useful time frame.

O

opaque A type of material that reflects or absorbs all of the light that strikes it.

orbit The path of an object as it revolves around another object in space.

overpopulation A condition in which the number of humans grows beyond what the available resources can support.

ozone A form of oxygen that has three oxygen atoms in each molecule instead of the usual two; toxic to organisms where it forms near Earth's surface.

P

penumbra The part of a shadow surrounding the darkest part.

period One of the units of geologic time into which geologists divide eras.

phase One of the different apparent shapes of the moon as seen from Earth.

pitch A description of how a sound is perceived as high or low.

pixel A small, uniform shape that is combined with other pixels to make a larger image.

planet An object that orbits a star, is large enough to have become rounded by its own gravity, and has cleared the area of its orbit.

point source A specific source of pollution that can be identified.

pollution Contamination of Earth's land, water, or air through the release of harmful substances into the environment.

potential energy Stored energy based on position or shape of an object.

protein Large organic molecule made of carbon, hydrogen, oxygen, nitrogen, and sometimes sulfur.

R

reference frame A place or object used for comparison to determine whether an object is in motion.

reflection The bouncing back of an object or a wave when it hits a surface through which it cannot pass.

refraction The bending of waves as they enter a new medium at an angle, caused by a change in speed.

relative age The age of a rock compared to the ages of other rocks.

renewable resource A resource that is either always available or is naturally replaced in a relatively short time.

reptile A vertebrate whose temperature is determined by the temperature of its environment, that has lungs and scaly skin, and that lays eggs on land.

resonance The increase in the amplitude of a vibration that occurs when external vibrations match an object's natural frequency.

revolution The movement of an object around another object.

rotation The spinning motion of a planet on its axis.

S

satellite An object that orbits a planet.

scientific theory A well-tested explanation for a wide range of observations or experimental results.

sediment Small, solid pieces of material that come from rocks or the remains of organisms; earth materials deposited by erosion.

sewage The water and human wastes that are washed down sinks, toilets, and showers.

sex chromosomes The pair of chromosomes carrying genes that determine whether a person is biologically male or female.

sex-linked gene A gene carried on a sex chromosome.

slope The steepness of a graph line; the ratio of the vertical change (the rise) to the horizontal change (the run).

software Programs that encode, decode, and interpret information.

solar system The system consisting of the sun and the planets and other objects that revolve around it.

solenoid A coil of wire with a current.

solstice Either of the two days of the year on which the sun reaches its greatest distance north or south of the equator.

species A group of similar organisms that can mate with each other and produce offspring that can also mate and reproduce.

speed The distance an object travels per unit of time.

standing wave A wave that appears to stand in one place, even though it is two waves interfering as they pass through each other.

star A ball of hot gas, primarily hydrogen and helium, that undergoes nuclear fusion.

GLOSSARY

static electricity A buildup of charges on an object.

sun A large, gaseous body at the center of the solar system.

sustainable Using a resource in ways that maintain it at a certain quality for a certain period of time.

sustainable use The practice of allowing renewable resources time to recover and replenish.

T

telescope An optical instrument that forms enlarged images of distant objects.

thermal pollution A type of pollution caused by factories and power plants releasing superheated water into bodies of water.

transformer A device that increases or decreases voltage, which often consists of two separate coils of insulated wires wrapped around an iron core.

transluscent A type of material that scatters light as it passes through.

transparent A type of material that transmits light without scattering it.

transverse wave A wave that moves the medium at right angles to the direction in which the wave travels.

U

umbra The darkest part of a shadow.

unconformity A gap in the geologic record that shows where rock layers have been lost due to erosion.

V

variation Any difference between individuals of the same species.

velocity Speed in a given direction.

vertebrate An animal with a backbone.

W

wave A disturbance that transfers energy from place to place.

wave pulse A pulse of energy that travels through an electric circuit when it is closed.

wavelength The distance between two corresponding parts of a wave, such as the distance between two crests.

weight A measure of the force of gravity acting on an object.

INDEX

* Page numbers for charts, graphs, maps, and pictures are printed in italics. Page numbers for definitions are printed in boldface.

INDEX

INDEX

CREDITS

Photography

Photo locators denoted as follows: Top (T), Center (C), Bottom (B), Left (L), Right (R), Background (Bkgd)

Covers

Front: Tntemerson/iStock/Getty Images; Rafe Swan/Getty Images; Stefan Christmann/Getty Images; Dudarev Mikhail/Shutterstock; Sumiko Scott/Getty Images; Back: Marinello/DigitalVision Vectors/Getty Images

Instructional Segment 3

iv: Nick Lundgren/Shutterstock; vi: Dr P. Marazzi/Science Source; vii: Tonyz20/Shutterstock; viii: Sinclair Stammers/Science Photo Library/Getty Images; xT: Fabriziobalconi/Fotolia; xBkgd: Brian J. Skerry/National Geographic/Getty Images; xi: Dale Kolke/ZUMA Press/Newscom; 000: The Natural History Museum/Alamy Stock Photo; 004TL: Sabena Jane Blackbird/Alamy Stock Photo; 004B: Science Stock Photography/Science Source; 004TCL: Sinclair Stammers/Science Source; 005T: Georg Gerster/Science Source; 005B: The Natural History Museum/Alamy Stock Photo; 006T: Mikkel Juul Jensen/Science Source; 006B: Brian J. Skerry/Getty Images; 008: Dr P. Marazzi/Science Source; 010: Cuppyuppycake Creative/Getty Images; 016TR: Miodrag Gajic/Getty Images; 016BR: MixAll Studio Creative/Getty Images; 018: Marc Moritsch/National Geographic Creative/Alamy Stock Photo; 020: Power and Syred/Science Source; 024BC: D. Kucharski & K. Kucharska/Shutterstock; 024BR: Dragon Images/Shutterstock; 025: Aquapix/Shutterstock; 026: Inga Ivanova/Shutterstock; 028: Eriklam/123RF; 030: Reuters/Alamy Stock Photo; 032BL: Eye of Science/Science Source; 032TR: Coneyl Jay/Getty Images; 033: Clive Gee/AP Images; 034: M. Watson/Ardea/AGE Fotostock; 039: Panther Media GmbH/Alamy Stock Photo; 048: Tonyz20/Shutterstock; 049: John Cancalosi/Alamy Stock Photo; 051Bkgrd: Jo Crebbin/Shutterstock; 051CL: Loop Images Ltd/Alamy Stock Photo; 052: Fototeca Gilardi/AKG Images; 054T: Holmes Garden Photos/Alamy Stock Photo; 054TCL: Russell Shively/Shutterstock; 056BC: Westend61/Getty Images; 056BR: Brian Kushner/Alamy Stock Photo; 060: Visual China Group/Getty Images; 062TL: Nature Photographers Ltd/Alamy Stock Photo; 062TC: Pises Tungittipokai/Shutterstock; 062TR: Oli Scarff/AFP/Getty Images; 063: Nature Photographers Ltd/Alamy Stock Photo; 064: IrinaK/Shutterstock; 066: Kali9/Getty Images; 067TL: Zeljko Radojko/Shutterstock; 067TC: Patricia Isaza; 068: IrinaK/Shutterstock; 069BCR: All Canada Photos/Alamy Stock Photo; 069TCR: Reuters/Ulises Rodriguez/Alamy Stock Photo; 070: imageBROKER/Alamy Stock Photo; 074BC: Sailorr/Shutterstock; 074TC: Bazzano Photography/Alamy Stock Photo; 074TR: Angel DiBilio/Shutterstock; 076: Martin Shields/Alamy Stock Photo; 077: Vodolaz/Fotolia; 078BC: YAY Media AS/Alamy Stock Photo; 078BR: Wwing/Getty Images; 079BC: Scott Camazine/Alamy Stock Photo; 079BL: The Science Picture Company/Alamy Stock Photo; 079BR: Fabian von Poser/Getty Images; 080: Bildagentur Zoonar GmbH/Shutterstock; 082BC: Steve Vidler/Alamy Stock Photo; 082BR: Pedro Bernardo/Shutterstock; 085CR: Barry Mansell/Nature Picture Library; 085TR: Michelle Gilders/Alamy Stock Photo; 086B: Wolfgang Polzer/Alamy Stock Photo; 086BR: Mark Carwardine/Getty Images; 086CL: Francois Gohier/VWPics/Alamy Stock Photo; 088: WaterFrame/Alamy Stock Photo; 093: Abeselom Zerit/Shutterstock; 095B: Don Johnston/Getty Images; 095CR: BGSmith/Shutterstock; 097: John Cancalosi/Science Source; 100BL: Gallinago_media/Shutterstock; 100BR: CLS Digital Arts/Shutterstock; 101: J Hindman/Shutterstock; 104: Sinclair Stammers/Science Photo Library/Getty Images; 106: Jim in SC/Shutterstock; 108BL: Carol Dembinsky/Dembinsky Photo Associates/Alamy Stock Photo; 108BR: Chris Curtis/Shutterstock; 114: Bernhard Edmaier/Science Source; 116BL: Chase Studio/Science Source; 116BR: Ralf Juergen Kraft/Shutterstock; 117TL: Jean-Philippe Delobelle/Alamy Stock Photo; 117TC: DEA/G. CIGOLINI/Getty Images; 117TR: Kevin Schafer/Alamy Stock Photo; 117BR: Catmando/Shutterstock; 118: Biophoto Associates/Science Source; 121: James King-Holmes/Science Source; 122: Laurie O'Keefe/Science Source; 124: MarcelClemens/Shutterstock; 125TL: John Cancalosi/Alamy Stock Photo; 125TR: Sabena Jane Blackbird/Alamy Stock Photo; 126TL: Stocktrek Images, Inc./Alamy Stock Photo; 126BR: Herschel Hoffmeyer/Shutterstock; 128TL: Jerry Young/Dorling Kindersley; 128B: The Natural History Museum/The Image Works; 129TC: Chase Studio/Science Source; 129C: Bedrock Studios/Dorling Kindersley; 129BC: Andreas Meyer/123RF; 131: Keith Arnold Photography/Moment/Getty Images; 136: Jonathan Blair/Getty Images; 137: Adwo/Shutterstock; 143L: iStock/Getty Images; 143R: Moose henderson/Shutterstock.

Take Notes

Take Notes

Use this space for recording notes and sketching out ideas.

Take Notes

Use this space for recording notes and sketching out ideas.

Take Notes

Take Notes

Use this space for recording notes and sketching out ideas.

Take Notes

Use this space for recording notes and sketching out ideas.

Take Notes